THE CHARLTON STANDARD CATALOGUE OF

BORDER FINE ARTS STORYBOOK FIGURINES

FIRST EDITION

BY
MARILYN SWEET

W.K. CROSS
PUBLISHER

The Charlton Press

TORONTO, ONTARIO · PALM HARBOR, FLORIDA

EDITORIAL

Editor	Jean Dale
Assistant Editor	Cindy Raycroft
Graphic Technician	Davina Rowan
Graphic Technician	Suzanne Powell

ACKNOWLEDGEMENTS

The Charlton Press and the author wish to thank those who have helped with the first edition of The Charlton Standard Catalogue of Border Fine Arts Storybook Figurines.

CONTRIBUTORS TO THE FIRST EDITION

The Publisher would like to thank the following individuals or companies who graciously supplied pricing, direct mail lists, photographs or allowed us access to their collections for photographic purposes. We offer sincere thanks to:

Carolyn Baker; Elizabeth Bart-Smith (Border Fine Arts Society); Harry Grainger; Jane Hill and the staff at ENESCO; Harry Leskauskas; Jane Mallot; Tina Merriman; Bruce Wheeler (Wheelers of Loughborough)

DISCLAIMERS

While every care has been taken to ensure accuracy in the compilation of the data in this catalogue, the author and the publisher cannot accept responsibility for errors and omissions.

A SPECIAL NOTE TO COLLECTORS

We welcome and appreciate any comments or suggestions in regard to The Charlton Standard Catalogue of Border Fine Arts Storybook Figurines. If you would like to participate in pricing or supplying previously unavailable data or information, please contact Jean Dale at (416) 488-1418, or e-mail us at chpress@charltonpress.com.

CANADIAN CATALOGUING IN PUBLICATION DATA

The Charlton standard catalogue of Border Fine Arts storybook figurines

Biennial.
1st ed.-
ISSN 1492-4641
ISBN 0-88968-247-X (2000 issue)

   1. Border Fine Arts — Catalogs. 2. Figurines—Scotland—Catalogs. I. Title: Border Fine Arts storybook figurines.

NK8473.S35C32   738.8'2'02941   C00-900675-3

The Charlton Press

EDITORIAL OFFICE
2040 Yonge Street, Suite 208, Toronto, Ontario M4S 1Z9 CANADA
Telephone: (416) 488-1418 Fax: (416) 488-4656
Telephone: (800) 442-6042 Fax: (800) 442-1542
www.charltonpress.com, e-mail: chpress@charltonpress.com

THE MILLENNIUM SNOW BALL

TABLE OF CONTENTS

HOW TO USE THIS CATALOGUE

THE LISTINGS

This book is designed to serve two specific purposes. First, to furnish the Border Fine Arts enthusiast with accurate listings containing vital information and photographs to aid in the building of a rewarding collection. Secondly, this publication provides BFA collectors and dealers with current market prices for Border Fine Arts Storybook Figurines.

Within the individual listings, the pieces are listed in alphabetical order. After the item's name comes **Modeller**, **Size, Colour(s)**, the date of **Issue** and withdrawal. The **Series** to which the piece belongs (if applicable) is listed next, followed by any **Variations**. Lastly, the suggested retail **Price** is given in American, Canadian and British funds.

VARIETY CLASSIFICATIONS

Collectors will note the following distinction concerning styles and versions:

STYLES: When two or more models have the same name but different physical modelling characteristics, they are listed as **Style One, Style Two** and so on after their names.

VERSIONS: Versions are modifications to a major style element.

VARIATIONS: Variations are modifications to a minor style element. A change in colour is a variation.

A WORD ON PRICING

In addition to providing accurate information, this catalogue gives readers the most up-to-date retail prices for Border Fine Arts Storybook Figurines in American, Canadian and British currencies.

To accomplish this, The Charlton Press continues to access an international pricing panel of experts that submits prices based on both dealer and collector retail-price activity, as well as current auction results. These market prices are carefully averaged to reflect accurate valuations in each of these three markets.

Please be aware that all prices given in a particular currency are for figures within that particular country. The prices published herein have not been calculated using exchange rates exclusively. They have been determined solely by supply and demand within the country in question.

A necessary word of caution. No pricing catalogue can be, or should be, a fixed price list. This catalogue, therefore, should be considered as a pricing guide only — showing the most current retail prices based on market demand within a particular region for the various items.

Current collectables, however, are priced differently in this catalogue. Such pieces are priced according to the manufacturer's suggested retail price in each of the three market regions. It should be noted that it is likely dealer discounting from these prices will occur.

One exception, however, occurs in the case of current models or recent limited editions issued in only one of the three markets. Since such items were priced by Border Fine Arts only in the country in which they were to be sold, prices for other markets are not shown.

The prices published herein are for pieces in mint condition. Collectors are cautioned that a repaired or restored piece may be worth as little as 25 per cent of the value of the same piece in mint condition. The collector interested strictly in investment potential will avoid damaged figurines.

THE INTERNET AND PRICING

The Internet is changing the way business is being done in the collectable marketplace. Linking millions of collectors around the world through chat rooms, antique and collector malls, Internet auctions and producer web sites, e-commerce has become big business.

Some of the effects caused by the Internet and e-commerce on the collectables business are as follows:

1. Collectors deal directly with other collectors, changing the dynamics of the traditional customer/dealer relationship.

2. Information concerning new issues, finds and varieties is readily available, twenty-four hours a day. Collectors' wants are made known instantly to a wide spectrum of dealers and collectors.

3. Prices:
   (a) Price differentials will disappear between global market areas as collectors and the delivery services team up to stretch the purchasing power of the collectable dollar/pound.
   (b) Prices of common to scarce items will adjust downward to compensate for the temporary expansion of merchandise supply. Conversely, prices of rare and extremely rare items will increase, a result of additional exposure to demand.
   (c) After a time even the prices of the common items will rise due to the growing worldwide demand for collectables.

4. Internet auction sites listing millions of items for sale on a daily basis continue to grow as more and more collectors discover the viability of using this method to buy and sell merchandise.

5. Traditional marketing strategies (retail stores, direct-mail retailers, collectable shows and fairs, and collectable magazines and papers) face increased pressure in a more competitive environment.

The Internet is user-friendly: no travelling required, twenty-four hour accessibility, no face-to-face contact or other pressure to buy or sell. Without a doubt, the arrival of e-commerce will change the way a collector adds to their collection.

INTRODUCTION
By Marilyn Sweet

I first became aware of Border Fine Arts on a trip to Scotland during the early '80s. I saw and admired many pieces in shops, and on enquiry found they were made in Langholm. Our route home was subsequently amended so that we could visit the home of Border Fine Arts! On arrival a local retailer directed us to the factory. It was late in the day, and the factory had just shut. A man came out to talk to us, invited us into his office, enthused about "Thorionware"™ and its properties, showed us some pieces and gave me some leaflets. That man was John Hammond - little did I realize then that 20 or so years later we would meet again to discuss the book you are now reading. In the intervening years I became a Border Fine Arts collector, not just of pieces but also of brochures, leaflets and price lists (in the case of the latter items my husband would say a "hoarderer" - but how useful my carefully "hoarded" items have now become for they form the basis of this book!) In every new town we visited the local stocklist was sought! I was well and truly hooked. I became a founder member of the BFA Society and attended many BFA events. I have visited Langholm and Border Fine Arts many times now, but it is that original occasion that still sticks in my mind, rather like John Hammond's own initial visit to Langholm. This book is the culmination of all these "Border Fine Arts" experiences and I hope that collectors old and new enjoy it alike!

THE HISTORY OF BORDER FINE ARTS

The Early Days

The tourist guide "Discover Eskdale and Liddesdale" begins with an excerpt from a poem which reads:

> "Amidst the rolling Cheviots,
> The town of Langhom lies.
> A little off the beaten track,
> That's why it's Paradise."

The guide continues: "It has often been likened to Brigadoon - such is its charm that visitors often fear that if they blink it could disappear in the mist." Mist has some importance to the story of "Border Fine Arts" ... without it Border Fine Arts almost certainly would not have been founded in Langholm or indeed in the Scottish Borders! Fate often takes a hand in the best-laid plans and it definitely played its part in connection with Border Fine Arts.

John Hammond, the founder of the company, was attracted to this place of peace and tranquility during a chance visit to the Borders. Langholm lies about 22 miles north of Carlisle and nestles in the hills beside the famous sea trout River Esk. John had come north investigating the possibilities of setting up a business making figurines. He had toured Northern England and arrived in the Lake District. Being so close to the Scottish border, he decided to cross it just to say he had been to Scotland! On his return

south, the mists descended and with visibility so poor he decided to find accommodation for the night. Staying overnight in Langholm, he was taken by the kindness, warmth and general friendliness of the Border people and he spent the next day exploring the area before returning south to Winchester.

A few short weeks later, John returned to see Middleholms, an 18th century farmhouse on the outskirts of Langholm which had outbuildings offering workshop potential. Middleholms was acquired — for once, the swirling Scottish mists had a positive outcome, as who knows what might have happened had John been able to safely journey south that night! John and sculptor Victor Hayton set up "Border Craft and Design," with just three employees and began to make cold-cast bronze and silver figurines in late 1972.

Middleholms

John travelled miles at the beginning promoting the company and gaining a foothold in the market. One day Jedburgh antique dealer Ron Turner informed him that "people likes 'em small and likes 'em painted." The advice was to be acted upon, and back at Middleholms he and the workforce discussed this. Experiments began to research materials and paint, the latter involving paint-makers in Portsmouth who specialised in anti-fouling paints. Finally, a special cold casting process was developed which allowed the sculptures to be subsequently painted. The material developed was named "Thorionware"™ and it offered the opportunity to make figurines with an incredible amount of detail. September 1974 was an important date for the company as that was when the name "Border Fine Arts" was registered.

In the early years Border Fine Arts was a very small craft operation based around the kitchen table at Middlehoms

Farm. John advertised locally for people with the ability to paint and found a wealth of talent in and around Langholm. The Border area has a long tradition of cloth dyeing and weaving, with its tweed being world famous. The Borderers' natural understanding of colour, with a little training, was quickly transferred to ceramic painting. The Company developed new designs which were carefully researched, well-detailed, and painted in natural colours. They were extremely well-received by a growning band of appreciative collectors. The workforce was expanded and Middleholms was filled to capacity.

Langholm

The 1977 price list (the earliest I have a copy of) was comprised of 24 Natural History Sculptures by Victor Hayton, with singular contributions from Anne Wall and Mairi Lang Hunt. It was produced on a typewriter with the few product codes in existence written on – far removed from the professional full-colour brochures of the future! Victor's Limited Editions included LO2 Red Squirrels (edition of 100) and Weasel and Wren (edition of 125), which makes these amongst the smallest edition numbers issued by Border. Few of the early pieces had a product code: however, LO1 (edition of 250) went to Peregrine Falcon, Border's first hand-painted piece. Depicting a falcon pinning down his prey, this impressive sculpture is highly sought after today, as are all of the early pieces.

New premises were soon required and, in 1978, Border Fine Arts moved to its present location, Townfoot, in Langholm itself. The initial buildings there also had to be added to as demand for Border Fine Arts products continued to increase. In 1986, Border Fine Arts won the Scottish Business Achievement Award in recognition of growth of the Company and commitment to making a quality product.

Subsidiary Companies/Merchanting Division

Around 1987, Border Fine Arts developed their "Merchanting Division," a subsidiary company based in Northampton. Here, The Chiltern Collection (including Thelwell's Riding Academy and the Flower Fairies) were manufactured. Over the years, the Merchanting Division have also marketed a wide variety of products including Flower Fairies fine bone china giftware, collectors plates from "American Artists," various art prints, Waterford Porcelain Dolls, The Lowell Davis Farm Collection, The Legend of King Arthur, and Pups and Dogs Galore. The collections of Finesse Bone China Birds and The Imagined World of Fleur Cowles were manufactured in Worcester. The Carrickfergus factory in Northern Ireland manufactured The Irish Heritage Collection, consisting of cottages, pubs, and historical monuments of Ireland as well as The Wee Folk and a small number of figurines. (For pieces not found in this catalogue, see The Charlton Standard Catalogue of Border Fine Arts Figurines, First Edition.)

ENESCO

In November 1995 Border Fine Arts became a division of Enesco European Giftware Group, Ltd. and the manufacturing of some products was completely transferred to the Far East. This included the Beatrix Potter range, Lowell Davis pieces, and Dogs, Cats and Kittens Galore. Enesco is one of the world's leading producers of giftware, collectables and decorative accessories. Their ranges include the well-known Cherished Teddies, David Winter Cottages and Lilliput Lane. Enesco had become associated with BFA in 1989, with BFA distributing Enesco's products in the U.K. Border Fine Arts own ranges were extended to include novelty type and decorative accessories, housewares and other ceramic items. In order to clarify the situation, John Hammond issued a letter in January 1999 to all BFA Society members. In this he explained that in recent years Border Fine Arts had diversified into new ranges of products marketed under the brand name "Border Fine Arts Studio." In order that they could be marketed at realistic prices, the products had to be sourced from high-quality manufacturers in the Orient. The traditional, James Herriot, wildlife and agricultural product on which Border Fine Arts' reputation is based would carry the name "Border Fine Arts Classic." This guaranteed such products were manufactured in the U.K. Hence, distinguishing the place of manufacture, which had until then been rather hazy with regard to some products, became crystal clear! Efforts have been made to establish the place of manufacture of the items contained in this book. Some have been listed as "Made in China" in price lists and brochures whilst others have this on the labels stuck to the underside of the piece and also mentioned on their package boxes. Within this book there are pieces that have only been manufactured initially in the U.K. and then manufacture has been transferred to China. The latter ones are evidenced by the reduction in price.

Hence some pieces have two prices listed in this book, one for the U.K. manufactured piece and one for the "Made Abroad" manufactured version.

MAKING A BORDER FINE ARTS FIGURINE

The inherent qualities of the Thorionware™ process allows the artist great scope for exciting and complex compositions previously impossible in ceramic sculptures. The sculptor uses a special modelling wax to make the original. The actual creation of the design can take many hours as every detail has to be carved by hand using intricate dentistry tools. The original wax sculpture then has to be approved.

The process begins with the "blocking" of the sculpture's original design. A special mould-making silicone compound is carefully applied over the wax original to produce the master mould. This is a crucial part of the process, as a mistake could result in the loss of the original and all the hours and hours of work it represents.

Having removed the wax original from the master mould, a metal composition casting is then poured which becomes the production master pattern. This master pattern is carefully worked with engraving tools to ensure that every detail is clear and accurate, and eventually forms the basis for the production process. Production moulds and cases are made with great precision from this master, for they must not distort in any way during the casting cycle.

BFA's unique resin Thorionware™ is injected as a liquid "slip" into the moulds. A chemical reaction takes place under pressure, which results in a white porcelain-like casting — a faithful rendering of the sculptor's original.

The whiteware castings in their moulds are then moved to the demoulding room. Here they are very carefully and skilfully removed (demoulded) and set aside to finish curing. They are also inspected and any piece not up to BFA's exacting standards will be destroyed. The moulds are reassembled and sent back to the casting room for further use.

The figurines are then carefully fettled using dentistry drills to remove excess material from the figurine. Any pieces composed of several parts may be assembled at this point. Precise quality controls are implemented at this time and all imperfect figurines are immediately discarded.

The surface of the sculpture is treated to accept the enamel paints. If the piece is a new addition, the whiteware goes back to the design studio where the master painter decorates the new piece under the guidance of the sculptor. Many "proofs" will be developed before one is decided upon as the production standard.

All Border Fine Arts sculptures are hand-painted from start to finish by highly trained artists. The artist uses a wide palette of special enamel colours to build up to the finished piece with several applications. Being individually hand-painted means that no two pieces will be identical. The studio manager continually inspects for quality and style. Finally, the painter initials the finished pieces. A small certificate signed by the painter accompanies many sculptures and certificates of prestigious pieces even have a small photograph of the artist.

In the finishing deparment any complicated sculptures which require painting in several parts are carefully assembled. A further quality check follows and then a clear enamel is applied before the sculptures are baked in an oven which fuses the colours to the body of the piece. This produces a durable and natural finish.

L-R: Louise Conroy, Ray Ayres and Marilyn Sweet, 1999

Where appropriate the pieces are mounted on fine mahogany bases. Limited editions are numbered and registered. The final quality check then takes place and the base is baized or felted to protect the purchaser's furniture. The sculptures are carefully packed to begin their journeys all over the world.

It is the attention to detail at every stage of the manufacturing process that has become the hallmark of Border Fine Arts. Throughout the world, Border Fine Arts is widely acknowledged for its "craftsmanship in sculpture" - truly the Collector's Choice.

BORDER FINE ARTS STORYBOOK FIGURINES

Beatrix Potter Collection

It is now over a hundred years since Beatrix Potter wrote a picture letter to the sick son of a former governess, four year old Noel Moore. In it she told the tale of four little rabbits by the names of Flopsy, Mopsy, Cotton-tail and Peter Rabbit. Eight years later she privately published "The Tale of Peter Rabbit." It was an immediate success, and as a result, Frederick Warne agreed to publish her book commercially provided that Beatrix redo the illustrations in colour. By the end of 1903, 50,000 copies of Peter Rabbit had been sold and it has never been out of print since! Beatrix went on using her talents as author and illustrator of many books about her animal characters.

In 1987 John Hammond was considering the possibility of adding to the Border Fine Arts range by introducing models of animal writers. He happened to have illustrations of Beatrix Potter's characters on his desk when Richard Wawrzesta, the Managing Director of Chiltern, BFA's Northampton subsidiary company, was attending a meeting. Richard suggested that he would like to attempt to model some of the Beatrix Potter subjects. Although he had never seriously sculpted before, his models met with the approval of Border Fine Arts and Frederick Warne. Richard Wawrzesta went on to model all the Beatrix Potter characters and indeed the Brambly Hedge ones too. The vast majority of the Border Fine Arts pieces in this book are his work.

BP12 The Amiable Guinea Pig

Richard was born in Northampton in 1952. He went to Art College and then tried several ventures of an artistic nature before becoming managing director of Chiltern.

The early Beatrix Potter Collection figurines were issued in beautiful painted gift tins that have become collectable in their own right. The initial models BP1 to BP12 were extended over the next few years until a total of 28 formed the main series entitled "The World of Beatrix Potter." The first retired models were BP10 Cecily Parsley Ran Away and BP12 The Amiable Guinea Pig, which were both withdrawn in December 1989. A year later, BP18 Henny Penny Meets Jemima Puddle-duck retired after being available for only two years. The last three figures in the series, BP26 Little Black Pig, BP27 Benjamin Bunny Eating Lettuce, and BP28 Old Mr. Bunny, also had very short production runs, making these very difficult to find today. "The World of Beatrix Potter Miniatures" forms quite an extensive collection of 37 models, 35 of which (prefixed by BPM) were manufactured by BFA in the U.K. The BFA Beatrix Potter Miniatures include a number of unique characters, including Kep the Collie Dog, Lucinda the Doll, Jane and Clock, and Cat with Watering Can. In 1993, 20 miniature figurines were issued

in five sets of vignettes with a three-dimensional cardboard display to accompany each vignette.

Following Enesco's acquisition of Border Fine Arts, manufacture transferred to the Far East, and the figures were considerably reduced in price. They lost their BPM prefix and were allocated a 6-figure number. These figures have "Made in China" printed on the underside of the base. Since 1998, however, special commissions have returned to the U.K. for production. These figures are larger and more expensive, and include two new intricate tableau pieces, both designed by Richard Wawrzesta in celebration of the millennium.

Brambly Hedge

Jill Barklem's series of books about the mouse community living in the English hedgerow of "Brambly Hedge" were published in 1980. The first four, Spring, Summer, Autumn and Winter, were such an immediate success that manufacturers were soon requesting licences to reproduce the characters in a variety of media. Richard Wawrzesta modelled some Brambly Hedge characters that were received with enthusiasm by Jill Barklem, who was impressed with the fine detail the Thorionware™ resin allowed. BFA's licence was issued in January 1987 and expired in December 1997. Richard Wawrzesta modelled the entire collection which was first issued in 1988 with the first five figures and three pieces of furniture of the Store Stump Kitchen Collection. The figures were initially packed in attractive metal tins. The pieces are impressed at the back "B.H.c J.B. date year B.F.A." A paper label is stuck to the underside of the base.

Furniture from the Brambly Hedge illustrations also joined the collection and again much detail was able to be included. Cardboard display stands of Brambly Hedge scenes could be purchased which gave the figurines a lovely background setting. These were withdrawn by 1992 and are sought after, but not easily found today. Other items were added to the range such as clocks, cameos, and water balls. From 1989 these novelty type items were often manufactured in collaboration with the Enesco Corporation. Enesco themselves also had their own licence to manufacture Brambly Hedge items. Their resin figurines were also modelled by Richard Wawrzesta and were the same as the Border Fine Arts designs. They were manufactured in China and were available mainly in the U.S.A. between 1990 and 1994. Whereas Enesco's figurines tend to have a waxy finish, the models produced by Border Fine Arts do not.

Fairies

The world of make-believe enjoyed a high profile in the 19th century. The existence of "little people" as featured in the works of Hans Christian Anderson, Lewis Carroll and J.M. Barrie brought them to the fore. Cicely Mary Barker (1985-1973) became the "flower fairy painter" in 1923 when her book of illustrations entitled "Flower Fairies of the Spring" was printed by Blackie. Cicely was the daughter of a partner in a seed company. She sent botanical specimens for identification to Kew Gardens and received others to paint. She had a convenient source of child models for her fairies, as her sister ran a kindergarten in the family home. Cicely regularly added new books to the Flower Fairy Series until the last one, "Flower Fairies of the Wayside" was published in 1948.

There are four Border Fine Arts fairies series. The initial four pieces were modelled by David Geenty (more well-known for his animal sculptures) as open editions and were listed as "Flower Fairies by Linda Pagett." These were issued in 1981 and retired in December 1982. The 13 initial "Flower Fairies", based on the designs of Cicely Mary Barker, were

Lavender Fairy, Style One

also modelled by David Geenty and they also had production runs lasting for two years only. Again they were open editions. There was a gap of three years before Cicely Mary Barker's Flower Fairies were produced again, and in 1993, Glenis Devereux's models were issued. These were all limited editions of 1,950. In January 2000, a series of six open edition Flower Fairies miniature figurines were issued.

The Fairies are all quite delicate designs, with thin stems and petals adorning the majority. Any being offered on the secondary market would require careful scrutiny to ascertain condition.

Oliver Otter and Friends

Kate Veale began her career as a commercial artist in a design studio in Leicester in the 1980s after studying history at Durham University. Here she was noticed and subsequently tutored by Roland Hilder, popular artist and director of Royle Publications. In 1988 she joined Gordon Fraser to work on the well-known greeting card range "Country Companions." Drawing her inspiration from a love of animals and vivid childhood memories of growing up in the English countryside, she wrote and illustrated a series of four books for children about Oliver Otter and his friends which were published by Sapling in 1996. The four books are

"Drew the Shrew and the Star," "Did you swim today Oliver Otter?", "Follow the Trail, Digsby the Mole," and "Will Squirrel's Big Fizz." Each of the four characters portrayed by Border Fine Arts feature in their own book. The model of Drew the Shrew also includes his friend Trevelyan the Newt. The Border Fine Arts range was issued in 1997 and included bookends, a clock, nurseryware and picture frames. The models included in this book were manufactured in China.

Peter Pan

In 1995 Glenis Devereux modelled six characters from J.M. Barrie's play "Peter Pan." In 1929 Barrie had donated all the rights of his play to the Great Ormond Street Children's Hospital, and the royalties from the sale of BFA's Peter Pan range were similarly to benefit this famous London hospital.

Ruff and Reddy

The antics of Ruff the Border Collie pup and his friend Reddy, a ginger and white kitten, were interpreted by long-time Border Fine Arts modeller Anne Wall and introduced in 1995. The set of 10 models depicts them getting involved in the typical mischief of young animals: for example, in RR04 Washday Blues, the two are pouncing on newly washed overalls to get them just like the farmer likes them — covered in mud and farmyard stains!

Thelwell

Norman Thelwell drew cartoons for "Punch" magazine and many of these were included in his books. "Thelwell's Riding Academy" and "Angels on Horseback" were just two of several books featuring rather plump little girls and their equally endowed shaggy and rather appealing ponies getting up to a wide variety of mischief. BFA's Chiltern Division accurately reproduced the humour in two series, "Thelwell's Riding Academy" and "Thelwell Goes West," the former featuring the English style of riding, whilst the latter half

Point of Departure, Thelwell's Riding Academy

dozen have cowboys! Thelwell's were initially modelled by Fred Moore; later models were the work of Richard Wawrzesta. Each piece is incised with Thelwell's signature and a copyright date. The underside of the base has a paper sticker giving the model name and number, which states "Made in England." Each year from 1984 to 1995, a special Christmas themed piece was issued. Several models had a production run of only a year and three lasted for just six months.

Wind in the Willows

These four figurines were based on Kenneth Graham's main riverbank characters of Ratty, Mole, Toad and Badger from his book "Wind in the Willows." Very little is known about the actual models. The series was entitled "Miniatures on Bronze," and a limited number were possibly issued between July and December 1983, making them very elusive today. Please note that M30 Ratty and M31 Mole share their allocated numbers with M30 Running Fox and M31 Otter from the "Miniatures on Bronze Animals" series (see The Charlton Standard Catalogue of Border Fine Arts Figurines, First Edition).

Winnie the Pooh

Alan Alexander (always known as A.A.) Milne's well-known stories of Winnie the Pooh were first published by Methuen in 1926. The stories were written for, and about, his son Christopher Robin, involving adventures with his teddy bear Winnie the Pooh and his companions from the nursery. Ernest Shepherd drew the original illustrations but he did not produce the coloured-in versions until 1973. Christopher Robin and his toy animal friends from the Hundred Acre Wood are still popular with today's children. Disney recently released another cartoon film based on the characters which has further stimulated enthusiasm. Children, and indeed adults too, are avid collectors of Winnie the Pooh merchandise. Like other characters covered by this book, many diverse producets have been manufactured over the years by a wide variety of companies on the Winnie the Pooh theme. In 2000, Border Fine Arts Studio issued their "Classic Pooh" collection. This consists of two quite distinct yet related product ranges: "Lifestyle", which are a selection of home decor accessories such as pencil boxes, candlesticks and mirrors with a Winnie the Pooh figurine as part of the piece, and "Figurines" featuring Pooh, Tigger, Piglet and Eeyore. As they are "Studio" pieces, they are manufactured abroad.

HOW TO COLLECT BORDER FINE ARTS STORYBOOK FIGURINES

There is a vast range of Border Fine Arts Storybook Figurines, and most collectors seem to specialize in one or two aspects. Many collectors prefer the traditional approach of collecting by series. While series such as Oliver Otter or The Legend of King Arthur are relatively small, the Beatrix Potter and Brambly Hedge ranges include a number of series large enough to occupy any new collector for some time! Collecting by subject, independent of series, is also quite common. This could result in a collection by type of character (i.e. Mrs. Tiggy-Winkle), or of commemorative pieces (i.e. Autumn) which were under limited release. Acquiring pieces of a certain size may also appeal to a collector: within the Beatrix Potter range, for example, there are Miniatures (the largest being 3" high) as well as the Money Banks (ranging from 4 ¼" to 7 ¾" high.)

CARE AND REPAIR

A Border Fine Arts collection can be enjoyed indefinitely as long as care is taken when handling and cleaning. When dusting in situ, a soft cosmetic brush or photographic lens brush is useful for getting into tight corners. Care should be taken not to knock models against each other, as this may cause breakage.

If the worst happens, a professional restorer should be consulted as they can work 'miracles' with damaged pieces. It follows that when buying pieces on the secondary market, it is advisable to check for restorations. Projecting details are the most vulnerable parts, so look at these areas carefully in a good light. Restored models should be priced less than perfect examples, according to the amount of damage and the quality of the repair. Always enquire about the condition of a piece when buying, as a reputable dealer will stand by any guarantees they give regarding restorations.

INSURING YOUR COLLECTABLES

As with any other valuables, making certain your collectables are protected is a very important concern. It is paramount that you display or store any fragile items in a secure place, preferably one safely away from traffic in the home.

Your collectables are most often covered under your basic homeowner's policy. There are generally three kinds of such policies: standard, broad and comprehensive. Each has its own specific deductible and terms.

Under a general policy, your collectables are considered contents and are covered for all of the perils listed under the contractual terms of your policy (fire, theft, water damage and so on).

CONTACTING BORDER FINE ARTS

ENESCO European Giftware Group Ltd.
Brunthill Road
Kingstown Industrial Estate
Carlisle
Cumbria
CA3 0EN
England
Tel.: (0) 1228 404040
Fax: (0) 1228 404080
Overseas Customer Services:
Tel.: 44 1228 404040
Fax: 44 1228 404080

The Border Fine Arts Society can be contacted at:

Border Fine Arts Society
Townfoot
Langholm
Dumfriesshire
DG13 0ET
Scotland
Tel.: (0) 13873 83000
Fax: (0) 13873 83030
e-mail: enquiries@borderfinearts.com
Website: www.borderfinearts.com

THE BORDER FINE ARTS SOCIETY

As a response to the interest shown by a group of avid collectors, and in order to encourage new collectors, the Border Fine Arts Society was launched by the company on June 1st, 1989. Members receive a copy of the Society magazine "The Borderer" twice a year. This full-colour publication contains a variety of articles on the modellers, the process, new models and promotions, local places of interest and traditions, and competitions. There is also a "Seekers" column whereby the members can list figurines they are seeking and the Society will receive communications on their behalf. The Society keeps members informed of Society Events and Painting Demonstrations which are held throughout the year at locations all over the U.K. (usually in connection with a BFA stocklist). Border Fine Arts Ray Ayres and Elizabeth Bart-Smith (Society Manager) often attend the larger ones and are always very willing to converse with anyone attending. Members receive a miniature figurine each year as part of the membership package and are entitled to purchase an Annual Society Figurine. To date, these have all been birds or wildlife models.

WHERE TO BUY

Border Fine Arts can be purchased from retail shops throughout the U.K. Many shops carry quite a range and can, of course, order anything in current production. Retailers are allocated pieces produced in limited editions. The Border Fine Arts Society will supply information of local retailers.

The market for secondary pieces is in its infancy at present, and such pieces are not readily obtainable. Odd pieces may be found at auctions and, occasionally, at general Collectors Fairs. The Border Fine Arts Society magazine carries a "Seekers" column; obviously, other transactions also occur on a private basis. There are a handful of specialist outlets offering secondary market pieces and currently one specialist auction. Internet auctions usually have pieces available.

FURTHER READING

Border Fine Arts Society Magazine "The Borderer"
Brambly Hedge Collectors Book, Louise Irvine
The Charlton Standard Catalogue of Border Fine Arts Figurines, First Edition, Marilyn Sweet

BEATRIX POTTER

Figurines
Cameos
Clocks
Money Banks
Musicals
Point of Sale Displays
Wall Plaques
Water Balls

FIGURINES
LARGE, IN TINS

This early series of Beatrix Potter figurines were produced in Scotland. They were packaged individually in tins, which were printed with scenes on the exterior.

THE AMIABLE GUINEA PIG™

TECHNICAL DATA

Model No.:	BP12
Modeller:	Richard Wawrzesta
Height:	3 ¾", 9.5 cm
Colour:	White and yellow guinea pig; mustard jacket; blue necktie and book; grey top hat; brown mirror
Issued:	Jan. 1987-Dec. 1989

PRICING DATA	U.K. £	U.S. $	Can. $
Made in U.K.	100.00	200.00	275.00

AUNT PETTITOES AND PIGLETS™
Style One

TECHNICAL DATA

Model No.:	BP2
Modeller:	Richard Wawrzesta
Height:	4 ¾", 12.1 cm
Colour:	Pink pig and piglets; blue and white striped dress and cap; white apron; grey pails
Issued:	Jan. 1987-Dec. 1993

PRICING DATA	U.K. £	U.S. $	Can. $
Made in U.K.	80.00	125.00	175.00

BENJAMIN BUNNY™

TECHNICAL DATA

Model No.:	BP14
Modeller:	Richard Wawrzesta
Height:	4 ½", 11.9 cm
Colour:	Brown and white rabbit; tan jacket; blue-green tam with a red pompon
Issued:	Jan. 1988-Dec. 1993

PRICING DATA	U.K. £	U.S. $	Can. $
Made in U.K.	65.00	95.00	130.00

FIGURINES
LARGE, IN TINS

CECILY PARSLEY RAN AWAY™

TECHNICAL DATA

Model No.:	BP10
Modeller:	Richard Wawrzesta
Height:	3 ½", 8.9 cm
Colour:	Brown rabbit; blue dress; white apron; brown wheelbarrow
Issued:	Jan. 1987-Dec. 1989

PRICING DATA	U.K. £	U.S. $	Can. $
Made in U.K.	100.00	150.00	200.00

COUSIN RIBBY™

TECHNICAL DATA

Model No.:	BP17
Modeller:	Richard Wawrzesta
Height:	4 ¼", 10.8 cm
Colour:	Ginger and brown cat; pink dress; green shawl, apron and umbrella
Issued:	Jan. 1989-Dec. 1993

PRICING DATA	U.K. £	U.S. $	Can. $
Made in U.K.	70.00	95.00	150.00

FOXY WHISKERED GENTLEMAN™
Style One

TECHNICAL DATA

Model No.:	BP19
Modeller:	Richard Wawrzesta
Height:	5", 12.7 cm
Colour:	Reddish-brown and white fox; green coat; red waistcoat; white trousers
Issued:	Jan. 1990-Dec. 1995

PRICING DATA	U.K. £	U.S. $	Can. $
Made in U.K.	70.00	95.00	150.00

FIGURINES
LARGE, IN TINS

HENNY PENNY MEETS JEMIMA PUDDLE-DUCK™

TECHNICAL DATA

Model No.:	BP18
Modeller:	Richard Wawrzesta
Height:	4", 10.1 cm
Colour:	Yellow chicken and chicks; grey apron; white duck; blue bonnet; rose and blue shawl
Issued:	Jan. 1989-Dec. 1990

PRICING DATA	U.K. £	U.S. $	Can. $
Made in U.K.	85.00	125.00	175.00

HUNCA MUNCA AND THE BABIES™
Style One

TECHNICAL DATA

Model No.:	BP5
Modeller:	Richard Wawrzesta
Height:	3", 7.6 cm
Colour:	Brown mice; blue dress; white apron and nightdress; pink blanket
Issued:	Jan. 1987-Dec. 1995

PRICING DATA	U.K. £	U.S. $	Can. $
Made in U.K.	85.00	125.00	175.00

HUNCA MUNCA SWEEPING™
Style One

TECHNICAL DATA

Model No.:	BP20
Modeller:	Richard Wawrzesta
Height:	4 ½", 11.9 cm
Colour:	Brown mouse; pink, white, green and cream clothing
Issued:	Jan. 1990-Dec. 1993

PRICING DATA	U.K. £	U.S. $	Can. $
Made in U.K.	85.00	125.00	175.00

FIGURINES
LARGE, IN TINS

JEMIMA PUDDLE-DUCK SETS OFF™

TECHNICAL DATA

Model No.:	BP7
Modeller:	Richard Wawrzesta
Height:	4", 10.1 cm
Colour:	White duck; blue bonnet; pink and blue shawl
Issued:	Jan. 1987-Dec. 1995

PRICING DATA	U.K. £	U.S. $	Can. $
Made in U.K.	70.00	95.00	150.00

JEREMY FISHER PUNTING™

TECHNICAL DATA

Model No.:	BP9
Modeller:	Richard Wawrzesta
Height:	2 ¾", 7.0 cm
Colour:	Yellow frog; white jacket and shirt; pink waistcoat
Issued:	Jan. 1987-Dec. 1993

PRICING DATA	U.K. £	U.S. $	Can. $
Made in U.K.	70.00	95.00	150.00

MISS MOPPET AND THE MOUSE™

TECHNICAL DATA

Model No.:	BP21
Modeller:	Richard Wawrzesta
Height:	4", 10.1 cm
Colour:	Brown and white kitten; pink bow; lilac handkerchief; rose stool; brown mouse: light green jacket; pink bowtie
Issued:	Jan. 1990-Dec. 1993

PRICING DATA	U.K. £	U.S. $	Can. $
Made in U.K.	70.00	100.00	150.00

FIGURINES
LARGE, IN TINS

MRS. RABBIT AT WORK™

TECHNICAL DATA

Model No.:	BP11
Modeller:	Richard Wawrzesta
Height:	4", 10.1 cm
Colour:	Blue dress; white and pink shawl; brown rabbits and table
Issued:	Jan. 1987-Dec. 1993

PRICING DATA	U.K. £	U.S. $	Can. $
Made in U.K.	85.00	125.00	175.00

MRS. TIGGY-WINKLE, THE WASHERWOMAN™

TECHNICAL DATA

Model No.:	BP6
Modeller:	Richard Wawrzesta
Height:	4", 10.1 cm
Colour:	Brown hedgehog; tan dresser and basket; white cap; pink, white, yellow and blue clothing; white apron
Issued:	Jan. 1987-Dec. 1990

PRICING DATA	U.K. £	U.S. $	Can. $
Made in U.K.	85.00	125.00	175.00

NUTKIN TICKLING OLD MR. BROWN™

TECHNICAL DATA

Model No.:	BP15
Modeller:	Richard Wawrzesta
Height:	3 ½", 8.9 cm
Colour:	Brown and cream owl; reddish-brown squirrel
Issued:	Jan. 1988-Dec. 1990

PRICING DATA	U.K. £	U.S. $	Can. $
Made in U.K.	100.00	150.00	200.00

FIGURINES
LARGE, IN TINS

OLD WOMAN WHO LIVED IN A SHOE™

TECHNICAL DATA

Model No.:	BP13
Modeller:	Richard Wawrzesta
Height:	4 ¾", 12.1 cm
Colour:	Blue shoe; brown mice; cream bonnet with pink bow
Issued:	Jan. 1988-Dec. 1995

PRICING DATA	U.K. £	U.S. $	Can. $
Made in U.K.	70.00	100.00	150.00

PETER RABBIT EATING A RADISH™

TECHNICAL DATA

Model No.:	BP16
Modeller:	Richard Wawrzesta
Height:	5", 12.7 cm
Colour:	Brown and white rabbit; blue jacket; red and brown robin on cream spade
Issued:	Jan. 1989-Dec. 1995

PRICING DATA	U.K. £	U.S. $	Can. $
Made in U.K.	65.00	85.00	125.00

PETER RABBIT IN THE GARDEN™
Style One

TECHNICAL DATA

Model No.:	BP1
Modeller:	Richard Wawrzesta
Height:	4 ½", 11.9 cm
Colour:	Brown and white rabbit; blue jacket; red handkerchief
Issued:	Jan. 1987-Dec. 1995

PRICING DATA	U.K. £	U.S. $	Can. $
Made in U.K.	65.00	85.00	125.00

FIGURINES
LARGE, IN TINS

TAILOR OF GLOUCESTER™
Style One

TECHNICAL DATA

Model No.:	BP3
Modeller:	Richard Wawrzesta
Height:	4 ½", 11.9 cm
Colour:	Brown mouse; tan spool of fuchsia thread; grey thimble
Issued:	Jan. 1987-Dec. 1995

PRICING DATA	U.K. £	U.S. $	Can. $
Made in U.K.	70.00	95.00	150.00

THIS ONE IS MOPPET™

TECHNICAL DATA

Model No.:	BP8
Modeller:	Richard Wawrzesta
Height:	3 ¾", 9.5 cm
Colour:	Tabby and ginger cats; purple dress; white apron and bowl; brown dresser
Issued:	Jan. 1987-Dec. 1993

PRICING DATA	U.K. £	U.S. $	Can. $
Made in U.K.	100.00	150.00	200.00

TIMMY WILLIE AND THE STRAWBERRY™

TECHNICAL DATA

Model No.:	BP4
Modeller:	Richard Wawrzesta
Height:	3 ½", 8.9 cm
Colour:	Brown and white mouse; red strawberry; green leaves
Issued:	Jan. 1987-Dec. 1995

PRICING DATA	U.K. £	U.S. $	Can. $
Made in U.K.	70.00	110.00	150.00

FIGURINES
LARGE, IN TINS

TIMMY WILLIE SLEEPING IN A PEA POD™

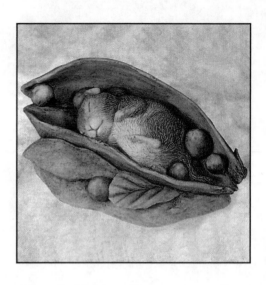

TECHNICAL DATA

Model No.:	BP22
Modeller:	Richard Wawrzesta
Height:	2", 5.0 cm
Colour:	Brown mouse; green pea pod
Issued:	Jan. 1991-Dec. 1995

PRICING DATA	U.K. £	U.S. $	Can. $
Made in U.K.	70.00	100.00	150.00

FIGURINES
LARGE, IN BOXES

BENJAMIN BUNNY EATING LETTUCE™

TECHNICAL DATA

Model No.:	BP27
Modeller:	Richard Wawrzesta
Height:	4 ¾", 12.1 cm
Colour:	Brown and white rabbit; brown jacket; green lettuce leaves
Issued:	Jan. 1994-Dec. 1995

PRICING DATA	U.K. £	U.S. $	Can. $
Made in U.K.	75.00	100.00	150.00

LADY MOUSE™

TECHNICAL DATA

Model No.:	BP24
Modeller:	Richard Wawrzesta
Height:	3 ¼", 8.3 cm
Colour:	Brown and white mouse; yellow, pink, blue and red clothing
Issued:	Jan. 1991-Dec. 1994

PRICING DATA	U.K. £	U.S. $	Can. $
Made in U.K.	75.00	100.00	150.00

LITTLE BLACK PIG (PIG-WIG)™

TECHNICAL DATA

Model No.:	BP26
Modeller:	Richard Wawrzesta
Height:	5", 12.7 cm
Colour:	Black and pink pig; blue dress
Issued:	Jan. 1994-Dec. 1995

PRICING DATA	U.K. £	U.S. $	Can. $
Made in U.K.	75.00	110.00	150.00

FIGURINES
LARGE, IN BOXES

OLD MR. BUNNY™

TECHNICAL DATA

Model No.:	BP28
Modeller:	Richard Wawrzesta
Height:	5 ¼", 13.3 cm
Colour:	Brown rabbit; violet jacket; cream and brown waistcoat; red handkerchief
Issued:	Jan. 1994-Dec. 1995

PRICING DATA	U.K. £	U.S. $	Can. $
Made in U.K.	70.00	100.00	150.00

TOM KITTEN WITH BUTTERFLY™

TECHNICAL DATA

Model No.:	BP23
Modeller:	Richard Wawrzesta
Height:	4 ½", 11.9 cm
Colour:	Brown kitten; blue suit; white collar; straw hat
Issued:	Jan. 1991-Dec. 1994

PRICING DATA	U.K. £	U.S. $	Can. $
Made in U.K.	70.00	100.00	150.00

FIGURINES
MEDIUM, IN TINS

In January 2000, the method of tin packaging was re-introduced with this range of new Beatrix Potter figurines.

HUNCA MUNCA SWEEPING™
Style Three

TECHNICAL DATA

Model No.:	739510
Modeller:	Richard Wawrzesta
Height:	3 ¾", 9.5 cm
Colour:	Brown mouse; pink dress; white apron; brown broom and dustbin
Issued:	Jan. 2000 to the present

PRICING DATA	U.K. £	U.S. $	Can. $
Made Abroad	19.95	—	—

JEMIMA PUDDLE-DUCK AND DUCKLINGS™

TECHNICAL DATA

Model No.:	739502
Modeller:	Richard Wawrzesta
Height:	3 ¾", 9.5 cm
Colour:	White duck; blue bonnet; rose-pink and blue shawl; yellow ducklings; pink flowers; green foliage
Issued:	Jan. 2000 to the present

PRICING DATA	U.K. £	U.S. $	Can. $
Made Abroad	19.95	—	—

MRS. RABBIT IN ROCKING CHAIR™

TECHNICAL DATA

Model No.:	739537
Modeller:	Richard Wawrzesta
Height:	3 ½", 8.9 cm
Colour:	Brown and white rabbits; blue dress; white apron; green lettuce in grey bowl
Issued:	Jan. 2000 to the present

PRICING DATA	U.K. £	U.S. $	Can. $
Made Abroad	19.95	—	—

FIGURINES
MEDIUM, IN TINS

MRS. TIGGY-WINKLE™
Style Two

TECHNICAL DATA

Model No.:	739529
Modeller:	Richard Wawrzesta
Height:	2 ¾", 7.0 cm
Colour:	Brown hedgehog; white cap; rose-pink, yellow and blue clothing; white cloth with blue trim
Issued:	Jan. 2000 to the present

PRICING DATA	U.K. £	U.S. $	Can. $
Made Abroad	19.95	—	—

PETER RABBIT IN THE GARDEN™
Style Two

TECHNICAL DATA

Model No.:	739499
Modeller:	Richard Wawrzesta
Height:	3 ¾", 9.5 cm
Colour:	Brown and white rabbit; blue jacket; red flowers; green leaves; brown and red bird; terra cotta planters
Issued:	Jan. 2000 to the present

PRICING DATA	U.K. £	U.S. $	Can. $
Made Abroad	19.95	—	—

TIMMY WILLIE™

TECHNICAL DATA

Model No.:	739545
Modeller:	Richard Wawrzesta
Height:	3 ¼", 8.3 cm
Colour:	Brown mouse; yellowish-green leaf; pink and white flowers
Issued:	Jan. 2000 to the present

PRICING DATA	U.K. £	U.S. $	Can. $
Made Abroad	19.95	—	—

FIGURINES
MINIATURES

AUNT PETTITOES AND PIGLETS™
Style Two

TECHNICAL DATA

Model No.:	BPM32/271764
Modeller:	Richard Wawrzesta
Height:	2 ½", 6.4 cm
Colour:	Pink pigs; blue and white clothing
Issued:	Jan. 1994 to the present

PRICING DATA	U.K. £	U.S. $	Can. $
Made in U.K.	25.00	40.00	60.00
Made Abroad	9.95	—	—

CAT WITH WATERING CAN™

TECHNICAL DATA

Model No.:	BPM10
Modeller:	Richard Wawrzesta
Height:	2 ½", 6.4 cm
Colour:	White cat; green watering can
Issued:	Jan. 1992-Dec. 1995
Story:	The Tale of Peter Rabbit

PRICING DATA	U.K. £	U.S. $	Can. $
Made in U.K.	25.00	40.00	60.00

FLOPSY, MOPSY AND COTTON-TAIL PICKING BLACKBERRIES™

TECHNICAL DATA

Model No.:	BPM26/271748
Modeller:	Richard Wawrzesta
Height:	2 ½", 6.4 cm
Colour:	Brown rabbits; salmon pink cloaks
Issued:	Jan. 1994 to the present

PRICING DATA	U.K. £	U.S. $	Can. $
Made in U.K.	25.00	40.00	60.00
Made Abroad	9.95	—	—

FIGURINES
MINIATURES

FLOPSY, MOPSY, COTTON-TAIL AND BOWL™

TECHNICAL DATA

Model No.:	BPM12/271845
Modeller:	Richard Wawrzesta
Height:	2", 5.0 cm
Colour:	Brown rabbits; white bibs and bowl
Issued:	Jan. 1992 to the present
Story:	The Tale of Peter Rabbit

PRICING DATA	U.K. £	U.S. $	Can. $
Made in U.K.	25.00	40.00	60.00
Made Abroad	9.95	—	—

FOXY WHISKERED GENTLEMAN™
Style Two

TECHNICAL DATA

Model No.:	BPM3/284149
Modeller:	Richard Wawrzesta
Height:	3", 7.6 cm
Colour:	Reddish-brown fox; green coat; white paper
Issued:	Jan. 1992 to the present
Story:	The Tale of Jemima Puddle-duck

PRICING DATA	U.K. £	U.S. $	Can. $
Made in U.K.	25.00	40.00	60.00
Made Abroad	9.95	—	—

GENTLEMAN MOUSE BOWING™

TECHNICAL DATA

Model No.:	BPM15
Modeller:	Richard Wawrzesta
Height:	2 ½", 6.4 cm
Colour:	Brown mouse; violet coat; white frills
Issued:	Jan. 1992-Dec. 1996
Story:	The Tailor of Gloucester

PRICING DATA	U.K. £	U.S. $	Can. $
Made in U.K.	25.00	40.00	60.00
Made Abroad	9.95	—	—

FIGURINES
MINIATURES

GINGER THE CAT™

TECHNICAL DATA

Model No.:	BPM18
Modeller:	Richard Wawrzesta
Height:	2 ¾", 7.0 cm
Colour:	Ginger tabby; olive green jacket; grey-blue parcel
Issued:	Jan. 1992-Dec. 1995
Story:	The Tale of Ginger and Pickles

PRICING DATA	U.K. £	U.S. $	Can. $
Made in U.K.	30.00	50.00	80.00

HUNCA MUNCA AND THE BABIES™
Style Two

TECHNICAL DATA

Model No.:	BPM7/271756
Modeller:	Richard Wawrzesta
Height:	2", 5.0 cm
Colour:	Brown mice; blue dress with cream trim; pink blanket; brown cradle
Issued:	Jan. 1992 to the present
Story:	The Tale of Two Bad Mice

PRICING DATA	U.K. £	U.S. $	Can. $
Made in U.K.	25.00	40.00	60.00
Made Abroad	9.95	—	—

HUNCA MUNCA SWEEPING™
Style Two

TECHNICAL DATA

Model No.:	BPM8
Modeller:	Richard Wawrzesta
Height:	2 ¼", 5.7 cm
Colour:	Brown mouse; lilac dress; white apron
Issued:	Jan. 1992-Dec. 1998
Story:	The Tale of Two Bad Mice

PRICING DATA	U.K. £	U.S. $	Can. $
Made in U.K.	25.00	40.00	60.00
Made Abroad	9.95	—	—

FIGURINES
MINIATURES

HUNCA MUNCA WITH RICE JAR™

TECHNICAL DATA

Model No.:	BPM22
Modeller:	Richard Wawrzesta
Height:	2 ½", 6.4 cm
Colour:	Brown mouse; turquoise jar
Issued:	Jan. 1993-Dec. 1995

PRICING DATA	U.K. £	U.S. $	Can. $
Made in U.K.	35.00	50.00	80.00

JANE AND CLOCK™

TECHNICAL DATA

Model No.:	BPM6
Modeller:	Richard Wawrzesta
Height:	3", 7.6 cm
Colour:	Pink dress; brown hair; tan clock
Issued:	Jan. 1992-Dec. 1993
Story:	The Tale of Two Bad Mice

PRICING DATA	U.K. £	U.S. $	Can. $
Made in U.K.	30.00	50.00	80.00

JEMIMA PUDDLE-DUCK™
Style One

TECHNICAL DATA

Model No.:	BPM2/271799
Modeller:	Richard Wawrzesta
Height:	3", 7.6 cm
Colour:	White duck; blue bonnet; rose and blue shawl
Issued:	Jan. 1992 to the present
Story:	The Tale of Jemima Puddle-duck

PRICING DATA	U.K. £	U.S. $	Can. $
Made in U.K.	25.00	40.00	60.00
Made Abroad	9.95	—	—

FIGURINES
MINIATURES

KEP THE COLLIE DOG™

TECHNICAL DATA

Model No.:	BPM1
Modeller:	Richard Wawrzesta
Height:	2 ½", 6.4 cm
Colour:	Brown, black and white dog; yellow ducklings
Issued:	Jan. 1992-Dec. 1993
Story:	The Tale of Jemima Puddle-duck

PRICING DATA	U.K. £	U.S. $	Can. $
Made in U.K.	30.00	50.00	80.00

LADY MOUSE CURTSEYING™

TECHNICAL DATA

Model No.:	BPM14
Modeller:	Richard Wawrzesta
Height:	2 ¼", 5.7 cm
Colour:	Brown mouse; cream and red dress; white apron and cap
Issued:	Jan. 1992-Dec. 1998
Story:	The Tailor of Gloucester

PRICING DATA	U.K. £	U.S. $	Can. $
Made in U.K.	25.00	40.00	60.00
Made Abroad	10.00	15.00	20.00

LUCINDA THE DOLL™

TECHNICAL DATA

Model No.:	BPM5
Modeller:	Richard Wawrzesta
Height:	2 ¾", 7.0 cm
Colour:	Blonde doll; blue and white dress
Issued:	Jan. 1992-Dec. 1993
Story:	The Tale of Two Bad Mice

PRICING DATA	U.K. £	U.S. $	Can. $
Made in U.K.	30.00	50.00	80.00

FIGURINES
MINIATURES

MR. JEREMY FISHER ON A BISCUIT TIN™

TECHNICAL DATA

Model No.: BPM17/271772
Modeller: Richard Wawrzesta
Height: 2 ½", 6.4 cm
Colour: Green frog; rose-pink
jacket; brown biscuit tin
Issued: Jan. 1992 to the present
Story: The Tale of Ginger and Pickles

PRICING DATA	U.K. £	U.S. $	Can. $
Made in U.K.	25.00	40.00	60.00
Made Abroad	9.95	—	—

MRS. RABBIT™

TECHNICAL DATA

Model No.: BPM11/284076
Modeller: Richard Wawrzesta
Height: 2 ½", 6.4 cm
Colour: Brown rabbit; orange-
brown dress; blue
overdress; red and
white shawl
Issued: Jan. 1992 to the present
Story: The Tale of Peter Rabbit

PRICING DATA	U.K. £	U.S. $	Can. $
Made in U.K.	25.00	40.00	60.00
Made Abroad	9.95	—	—

MRS. RABBIT AND PETER™
Second Variation

TECHNICAL DATA

Model No.: BPM28/271780
Modeller: Richard Wawrzesta
Height: 2 ¾", 7.0 cm
Colour: Brown rabbits; blue
and white clothing
Issued: Jan. 1994 to the present

PRICING DATA	U.K. £	U.S. $	Can. $
Made in U.K.	30.00	50.00	80.00
Made Abroad	9.95	—	—

FIGURINES
MINIATURES

MRS. TIGGY-WINKLE™
Style One

TECHNICAL DATA

Model No.:	BPM20
Modeller:	Richard Wawrzesta
Height:	2 ½", 6.4 cm
Colour:	Brown hedgehog; pink and white clothing; brown sack
Issued:	Jan. 1992-Dec. 1995
Story:	The Tale of Ginger and Pickles

PRICING DATA	U.K. £	U.S. $	Can. $
Made in U.K.	30.00	50.00	80.00

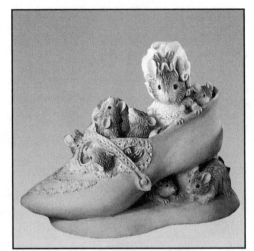

OLD WOMAN IN A SHOE™

TECHNICAL DATA

Model No.:	643904
Modeller:	Richard Wawrzesta
Height:	2 ¾", 7.0 cm
Colour:	Old Woman: brown; cream bonnet; Children: brown; Blue shoe
Issued:	June 1999 to the present

PRICING DATA	U.K. £	U.S. $	Can. $
Made Abroad	9.95	—	—

PETER RABBIT™
Style One

TECHNICAL DATA

Model No.:	BPM9/284238
Modeller:	Richard Wawrzesta
Height:	3 ¼", 8.3 cm
Colour:	Brown rabbit; blue jacket; red radishes
Issued:	Jan. 1992 to the present
Story:	The Tale of Peter Rabbit

PRICING DATA	U.K. £	U.S. $	Can. $
Made in U.K.	25.00	40.00	60.00
Made Abroad	9.95	—	—

FIGURINES
MINIATURES

PETER RABBIT EATING LETTUCE™
Second Variation

TECHNICAL DATA

Model No.:	BPM27/284157
Modeller:	Richard Wawrzesta
Height:	3 ¼", 8.3 cm
Colour:	Brown rabbit; blue jacket; green lettuce leaves
Issued:	Jan. 1994-Dec. 1999

PRICING DATA	U.K. £	U.S. $	Can. $
Made in U.K.	30.00	50.00	80.00
Made Abroad	10.00	15.00	20.00

PETER RABBIT IN WATERING CAN™
Second Version

TECHNICAL DATA

Model No.:	BPM24/271837
Modeller:	Richard Wawrzesta
Height:	2 ¾", 7.0 cm
Colour:	Brown rabbit; green watering can; brown pots
Issued:	Jan. 1994 to the present

PRICING DATA	U.K. £	U.S. $	Can. $
Made in U.K.	30.00	50.00	80.00
Made Abroad	9.95	—	—

PETER RABBIT IN WHEELBARROW™
Second Version

TECHNICAL DATA

Model No.:	BPM25/271810
Modeller:	Richard Wawrzesta
Height:	2 ¾", 7.0 cm
Colour:	Brown rabbit; green leaves
Issued:	Jan. 1994 to the present

PRICING DATA	U.K. £	U.S. $	Can. $
Made in U.K.	40.00	65.00	90.00
Made Abroad	9.95	—	—

FIGURINES
MINIATURES

PETER RABBIT RUNNING™
Second Version

TECHNICAL DATA

Model No.:	BPM29/284246
Modeller:	Richard Wawrzesta
Height:	3", 7.6 cm
Colour:	Brown rabbit; blue jacket and slippers
Issued:	Jan. 1994-Dec. 1999

PRICING DATA	U.K. £	U.S. $	Can. $
Made in U.K.	30.00	50.00	80.00
Made Abroad	10.00	15.00	20.00

PETER RABBIT STANDING™
Second Variation

TECHNICAL DATA

Model No.:	BPM30
Modeller:	Richard Wawrzesta
Height:	3", 7.6 cm
Colour:	Brown rabbit; blue jacket
Issued:	Jan. 1994-Dec. 1998

PRICING DATA	U.K. £	U.S. $	Can. $
Made in U.K.	30.00	50.00	80.00
Made Abroad	10.00	15.00	20.00

PETER RABBIT WITH ONIONS™

TECHNICAL DATA

Model No.:	BPM31/284165
Modeller:	Richard Wawrzesta
Height:	3", 7.6 cm
Colour:	Brown rabbit; blue jacket; red handkerchief
Issued:	Jan. 1994 to the present

PRICING DATA	U.K. £	U.S. $	Can. $
Made in U.K.	30.00	50.00	80.00
Made Abroad	9.95	—	—

FIGURINES
MINIATURES

PICKLES THE DOG™

TECHNICAL DATA

Model No.:	BPM23
Modeller:	Richard Wawrzesta
Height:	3", 7.6 cm
Colour:	Brown and white dog; tan coat; white apron
Issued:	Jan. 1993-Dec. 1995

PRICING DATA	U.K. £	U.S. $	Can. $
Made in U.K.	30.00	50.00	80.00

PIGLING BLAND™

TECHNICAL DATA

Model No.:	BPM33
Modeller:	Richard Wawrzesta
Height:	3", 7.6 cm
Colour:	Pink pig; blue and white waistcoat; umber jacket
Issued:	Jan. 1994-Dec. 1998

PRICING DATA	U.K. £	U.S. $	Can. $
Made in U.K.	25.00	40.00	60.00
Made Abroad	10.00	15.00	20.00

PIG-WIG DANCING™

TECHNICAL DATA

Model No.:	BPM34
Modeller:	Richard Wawrzesta
Height:	3", 7.6 cm
Colour:	Black and pink pig; blue and white dress
Issued:	Jan. 1994-Dec. 1996

PRICING DATA	U.K. £	U.S. $	Can. $
Made in U.K.	25.00	40.00	60.00
Made Abroad	10.00	15.00	20.00

FIGURINES
MINIATURES

REBECCA AND DUCKLINGS™

TECHNICAL DATA

Model No,:	BPM21
Modeller:	Richard Wawrzesta
Height:	2 ¾", 7.0 cm
Colour:	White duck; yellow ducklings
Issued:	Jan. 1993-Dec. 1995

PRICING DATA	U.K. £	U.S. $	Can. $
Made in U.K.	25.00	40.00	60.00

SALLY HENNY PENNY™

TECHNICAL DATA

Model No.:	BPM19
Modeller:	Richard Wawrzesta
Height:	3", 7.6 cm
Colour:	Yellow hen; black apron; yellow chicks
Issued:	Jan. 1992-Dec. 1995
Story:	The Tale of Ginger and Pickles

PRICING DATA	U.K. £	U.S. $	Can. $
Made in U.K.	20.00	35.00	50.00

SIMPKIN HOLDING A CUP™

TECHNICAL DATA

Model No.:	BPM16
Modeller:	Richard Wawrzesta
Height:	2 ½", 6.4 cm
Colour:	Tabby cat; white and pink cup
Issued:	Jan. 1992-Dec. 1995
Story:	The Tailor of Gloucester

PRICING DATA	U.K. £	U.S. $	Can. $
Made in U.K.	30.00	50.00	80.00

FIGURINES
MINIATURES

THE TAILOR OF GLOUCESTER™
Style Two

TECHNICAL DATA

Model No.:	BPM13/271829
Modeller:	Richard Wawrzesta
Height:	3", 7.6 cm
Colour:	Brown mouse; tan spool of fuchsia thread
Issued:	Jan. 1992 to the present
Story:	The Tailor of Gloucester

PRICING DATA	U.K. £	U.S. $	Can. $
Made in U.K.	25.00	40.00	60.00
Made Abroad	9.95	—	—

TIMMY WILLIE IN PEA POD™

TECHNICAL DATA

Model No.:	643920
Modeller:	Richard Wawrzesta
Height:	1 ½", 3.9 cm
Colour:	Brown and white mouse; green pea pod
Issued:	June 1999 to the present

PRICING DATA	U.K. £	U.S. $	Can. $
Made Abroad	9.95	—	—

FIGURINES
MINIATURES

TOM THUMB AND TONGS™

TECHNICAL DATA

Model No.:	BPM4
Modeller:	Richard Wawrzesta
Height:	3", 7.6 cm
Colour:	Brown and white mouse; gold tongs
Issued:	Jan. 1992-Dec. 1995
Story:	The Tale of Two Bad Mice

PRICING DATA	U.K. £	U.S. $	Can. $
Made in U.K.	25.00	40.00	60.00

YOCK-YOCK IN CLOTHES BASKET™

TECHNICAL DATA

Model No.:	BPM35
Modeller:	Richard Wawrzesta
Height:	1 ¾", 4.4 cm
Colour:	Pink pig; white towel; brown basket
Issued:	Jan. 1994-Dec. 1996
Story:	The Tale of Pigling Bland

PRICING DATA	U.K. £	U.S. $	Can. $
Made in U.K.	25.00	40.00	60.00
Made Abroad	10.00	15.00	20.00

FIGURINES
LIMITED EDITIONS

A LITTLE SHOE-HOUSE™

TECHNICAL DATA

Model No.:	120010
Modeller:	Richard Wawrzesta
Height:	4 ¾", 12.1 cm
Colour:	Blue shoe; brown mice; white cap with pink bow; blue and cream rug; brown floorboards; 22-carat gold button
Issued:	1998 in a limited edition of 1,250

PRICING DATA	U.K. £	U.S. $	Can. $
Made in U.K.	55.00	95.00	125.00

Note: Exclusive to Peter Rabbit and Friends.

BEATRIX POTTER MILLENNIUM TABLEAU™

TECHNICAL DATA

Model No.:	669814
Modeller:	Richard Wawrzesta
Height:	6 ¼", 15.9 cm
Colour:	Figurines: brown, blue, red, tan, rose-pink, and yellowish-green; cream tableau; green grass
Issued:	1999 in a limited edition of 2,000

PRICING DATA	U.K. £	U.S. $	Can. $
Made in U.K.	80.00	135.00	175.00

CHRISTMAS TREE DANCE MILLENNIUM TABLEAU™

TECHNICAL DATA

Model No.:	120020
Modeller:	Richard Wawrzesta
Height:	5 ½" x 7", 14.0 x 17.8 cm
Colour:	Figurines: blue, brown, white, rose-pink, green, yellow and tan; green tree with white snow and gold balls
Issued:	2000 in a limited edition of 500

PRICING DATA	U.K. £	U.S. $	Can. $
Made in U.K.	150.00	—	—

Note: Exclusive to Peter Rabbit and Friends.

FIGURINES
LIMITED EDITIONS

THE FLOPSY BUNNIES™

TECHNICAL DATA

Model No.:	120015
Modeller:	Richard Wawrzesta
Height:	3 ¾", 9.5 cm
Colour:	Brown and white bunnies (six); green foliage
Issued:	1999 in a limited edition of 999

PRICING DATA	U.K. £	U.S. $	Can. $
Made in U.K.	65.00	100.00	150.00

Note: Exclusive to Peter Rabbit and Friends.

FLOPSY, MOPSY AND COTTON-TAIL™

TECHNICAL DATA

Model No.:	CBP09
Modeller:	Richard Wawrzesta
Height:	3 ¾", 9.5 cm
Colour:	Brown rabbits; salmon cloaks
Issued:	Jan. 1993-Dec. 1993
Series:	100th Anniversary of Peter Rabbit (1893-1993)

PRICING DATA	U.K. £	U.S. $	Can. $
Made in U.K.	75.00	125.00	175.00

HILL TOP COTTAGE™

TECHNICAL DATA

Model No.:	CBP15
Modeller:	Richard Young
Height:	4", 10.1 cm
Colour:	Grey, brown and green
Issued:	Jan. 1993 in a limited edition of 1,993
Series:	100th Anniversary of Peter Rabbit (1893-1993)

PRICING DATA	U.K. £	U.S. $	Can. $
Made in U.K.	80.00	135.00	175.00

FIGURINES
LIMITED EDITIONS

JEMIMA PUDDLE-DUCK AND FOXGLOVES™

TECHNICAL DATA

Model No.:	120005
Modeller:	Richard Wawrzesta
Height:	4 ½", 11.9 cm
Colour:	White duck; rose-pink and blue shawl; blue bonnet; pink foxgloves; green foliage; grey stones; 22-carat gold brooch
Issued:	1998 in a limited edition of 1,250

PRICING DATA	U.K. £	U.S. $	Can. $
Made in U.K.	40.00	65.00	90.00

Note: Exclusive to Peter Rabbit and Friends.

MRS. RABBIT AND HER CHILDREN™

TECHNICAL DATA

Model No.:	BPLE01
Modeller:	Richard Wawrzesta
Height:	4 ¾", 12.1 cm
Colour:	Brown rabbits; blue, white and red clothing
Issued:	July 1995 in a limited edition of 2,500

PRICING DATA	U.K. £	U.S. $	Can. $
Made in U.K.	90.00	150.00	200.00

MRS. RABBIT AND PETER™
First Variation

TECHNICAL DATA

Model No.:	CBP11
Modeller:	Richard Wawrzesta
Height:	3 ¼", 8.3 cm
Colour:	Brown rabbits; blue and white clothing
Issued:	Jan. 1993-Dec. 1993
Series:	100th Anniversary of Peter Rabbit (1893-1993)

PRICING DATA	U.K. £	U.S. $	Can. $
Made in U.K.	65.00	100.00	150.00

FIGURINES
LIMITED EDITIONS

PETER AND WHEELBARROW™

TECHNICAL DATA

Model No.:	BP33
Modeller:	Richard Wawrzesta
Height:	5 ¾", 14.6 cm
Colour:	Brown and white rabbit; brown wheelbarrow; green leaves
Issued:	Jan. 1995 in a limited edition of 9,500

PRICING DATA	U.K. £	U.S. $	Can. $
Made in U.K.	60.00	95.00	125.00

PETER RABBIT™
Style Two

TECHNICAL DATA

Model No.:	CBP01
Modeller:	Richard Wawrzesta
Height:	7 ½", 19.1 cm
Colour:	Brown rabbit; blue jacket; red radishes; green leaves
Issued:	Jan. 1993 in a limited edition of 1,993
Series:	100th Anniversary of Peter Rabbit (1893-1993)

PRICING DATA	U.K. £	U.S. $	Can. $
Made in U.K.	75.00	125.00	175.00

PETER RABBIT EATING LETTUCE™
First Variation

TECHNICAL DATA

Model No.:	CBP12
Modeller:	Richard Wawrzesta
Height:	3 ¼", 8.3 cm
Colour:	Brown rabbit; blue jacket; green lettuce leaves
Issued:	Jan. 1993-Dec. 1993
Series:	100th Anniversary of Peter Rabbit (1893-1993)

PRICING DATA	U.K. £	U.S. $	Can. $
Made in U.K.	65.00	100.00	150.00

FIGURINES
LIMITED EDITIONS

PETER RABBIT IN MR. MCGREGOR'S GARDEN™

TECHNICAL DATA

Model No.:	BP25
Modeller:	Richard Wawrzesta
Height:	5 ¾", 14.6 cm
Colour:	Brown rabbit; blue jacket; red radishes; tan spade; brown and red robin
Issued:	Jan. 1996 in a limited edition of 9,500

PRICING DATA	U.K. £	U.S. $	Can. $
Made in U.K.	50.00	80.00	110.00

PETER RABBIT IN WATERING CAN™
First Version

TECHNICAL DATA

Model No.:	CBP07
Modeller:	Richard Wawrzesta
Height:	3 ½", 8.9 cm
Colour:	Brown rabbit; green watering can; brown pots
Issued:	Jan. 1993-Dec. 1993
Series:	100th Anniversary of Peter Rabbit (1893-1993)

PRICING DATA	U.K. £	U.S. $	Can. $
Made in U.K.	60.00	95.00	125.00

PETER RABBIT IN WHEELBARROW™
First Version

TECHNICAL DATA

Model No.:	CBP08
Modeller:	Richard Wawrzesta
Height:	3 ½", 8.9 cm
Colour:	Brown rabbit and wheelbarrow; green leaves; white cloth
Issued:	Jan. 1993-Dec. 1993
Series:	100th Anniversary of Peter Rabbit (1893-1993)

PRICING DATA	U.K. £	U.S. $	Can. $
Made in U.K.	60.00	95.00	125.00

FIGURINES
LIMITED EDITIONS

PETER RABBIT RUNNING™
First Version

TECHNICAL DATA

Model No.:	CBP13
Modeller:	Richard Wawrzesta
Height:	3 ½", 8.9 cm
Colour:	Brown rabbit; blue jacket and slippers
Issued:	Jan. 1993-Dec. 1993
Series:	100th Anniversary of Peter Rabbit (1893-1993)

PRICING DATA	U.K. £	U.S. $	Can. $
Made in U.K.	60.00	95.00	125.00

PETER RABBIT STANDING
First Variation

TECHNICAL DATA

Model No.:	CBP14
Modeller:	Richard Wawrzesta
Height:	3 ¾", 9.5 cm
Colour:	Brown rabbit; blue jacket and slippers
Issued:	Jan. 1993-Dec. 1993
Series:	100th Anniversary of Peter Rabbit (1893-1993)

PRICING DATA	U.K. £	U.S. $	Can. $
Made in U.K.	60.00	95.00	125.00

PETER RABBIT WITH FAMILY™

TECHNICAL DATA

Model No.:	Unknown
Modeller:	Richard Wawrzesta
Height:	4", 10.1 cm
Colour:	Brown rabbits; blue dress and jacket; white apron and bottle
Issued:	1991 in a limited edition of 1,200

PRICING DATA	U.K. £	U.S. $	Can. $
Made in U.K.	100.00	150.00	200.00

Note: Exclusive to Mead Johnson.

FIGURINES
LIMITED EDITIONS

PETER RABBIT WITH RADISHES™

TECHNICAL DATA

Model No.:	CBP10
Modeller:	Richard Wawrzesta
Height:	3 ¾", 9.5 cm
Colour:	Brown rabbit and spade handle; red radishes; red and brown robin
Issued:	Jan. 1993-Dec. 1993
Series:	100th Anniversary of Peter Rabbit (1893-1993)

PRICING DATA	U.K. £	U.S. $	Can. $
Made in U.K.	60.00	95.00	125.00

PETER SQUEEZED UNDER GATE™

TECHNICAL DATA

Model No.:	BP29
Modeller:	Richard Wawrzesta
Height:	5", 12.7 cm
Colour:	Brown rabbit; blue jacket; yellowish-brown gate; green foliage
Issued:	Jan. 1995 in a limited edition of 9,500

PRICING DATA	U.K. £	U.S. $	Can. $
Made in U.K.	70.00	110.00	150.00

PETER'S HIDING PLACE™

TECHNICAL DATA

Model No.:	BP32
Modeller:	Richard Wawrzesta
Height:	5", 12.7 cm
Colour:	Brown rabbit; grey-green watering can; brown flower pots
Issued:	Jan. 1995 in a limited edition of 9,500

PRICING DATA	U.K. £	U.S. $	Can. $
Made in U.K.	60.00	95.00	125.00

FIGURINES
ARCHWAY

AUNT PETTITOES™

TECHNICAL DATA

Model No.:	739553
Modeller:	Richard Wawrzesta
Height:	3 ½", 8.9 cm
Colour:	Pink pig; blue and white striped dress; white apron; green archway with blue flowers
Issued:	Jan. 2000 to the present

PRICING DATA	U.K. £	U.S. $	Can. $
Made Abroad	14.95	—	—

JEMIMA PUDDLE-DUCK™

TECHNICAL DATA

Model No.:	512044
Modeller:	Richard Wawrzesta
Height:	4", 10.1 cm
Colour:	White duck; blue bonnet; rose and blue shawl; rose-pink, green and brown archway
Issued:	Jan. 1999 to the present

PRICING DATA	U.K. £	U.S. $	Can. $
Made Abroad	14.95	—	—

MR. JEREMY FISHER™

TECHNICAL DATA

Model No.:	511897
Modeller:	Richard Wawrzesta
Height:	3 ½", 8.9 cm
Colour:	Yellow frog; rose-pink jacket; white paper; yellow, green, and brown archway
Issued:	Jan. 1999 to the present

PRICING DATA	U.K. £	U.S. $	Can. $
Made Abroad	14.95	—	—

FIGURINES
ARCHWAY

MRS. TIGGY-WINKLE™

TECHNICAL DATA

Model No.:	512656
Modeller:	Richard Wawrzesta
Height:	3 ½", 8.9 cm
Colour:	White cap; pink, white, yellow and blue outfit; lilac, blue and green archway
Issued:	Jan. 1999 to the present

PRICING DATA	U.K. £	U.S. $	Can. $
Made Abroad	14.95	—	—

PETER RABBIT™

TECHNICAL DATA

Model No.:	511900
Modeller:	Richard Wawrzesta
Height:	3 ½", 8.9 cm
Colour:	Brown rabbit; blue coat; rose-pink handkerchief; green and rose-pink archway
Issued:	Jan. 1999 to the present

PRICING DATA	U.K. £	U.S. $	Can. $
Made Abroad	14.95	—	—

PETER RABBIT WITH RADISH™

TECHNICAL DATA

Model No.:	739596
Modeller:	Richard Wawrzesta
Height:	3 ¾", 9.5 cm
Colour:	Brown rabbit; blue jacket; red radishes; orange and brown bird; green leaves
Issued:	Jan. 2000 to the present

PRICING DATA	U.K. £	U.S. $	Can. $
Made Abroad	14.95	—	—

FIGURINES
ARCHWAY

THE TAILOR OF GLOUCESTER™

TECHNICAL DATA

Model No.:	739561
Modeller:	Richard Wawrzesta
Height:	3 ½", 8.9 cm
Colour:	Brown mouse; white paper; tan spool of fuchsia thread; brown window frame with blue curtains
Issued:	Jan. 2000 to the present

PRICING DATA	U.K. £	U.S. $	Can. $
Made Abroad	14.95	—	—

TIMMY WILLIE™

TECHNICAL DATA

Model No.:	739588
Modeller:	Richard Wawrzesta
Height:	3 ¼", 8.3 cm
Colour:	Brown mouse; red strawberries; green leaves with white flowers
Issued:	Jan. 2000 to the present

PRICING DATA	U.K. £	U.S. $	Can. $
Made Abroad	14.95	—	—

FIGURINES
GROWING UP

NEW BABY (HUNCA MUNCA)™

TECHNICAL DATA

Model No.:	269425
Modeller:	Richard Wawrzesta
Height:	2 ¾", 7.0 cm
Colour:	Mother: brown; blue dress; white apron and trim Baby: brown; white nightgown
Issued:	June 1997 to the present
Series:	Nursery Collection

PRICING DATA	U.K. £	U.S. $	Can. $
Made Abroad	14.95	—	—

AGE 1 (CURIOUS RABBIT)™

TECHNICAL DATA

Model No.:	269433
Modeller:	Richard Wawrzesta
Height:	3 ¼", 8.3 cm
Colour:	Brown rabbit; blue coat; red handkerchief
Issued:	June 1997 to the present
Series:	Nursery Collection

PRICING DATA	U.K. £	U.S. $	Can. $
Made Abroad	14.95	—	—

AGE 2 (BAD MICE)™

TECHNICAL DATA

Model No.:	269441
Modeller:	Richard Wawrzesta
Height:	3 ½", 8.9 cm
Colour:	Brown mouse; tan plate; grey fish; brown chair
Issued:	June 1997-Dec. 1999

PRICING DATA	U.K. £	U.S. $	Can. $
Made Abroad	15.00	25.00	35.00

FIGURINES
GROWING UP

AGE 3 (PLAYFUL KITTEN)™

TECHNICAL DATA

Model No.:	269468
Modeller:	Richard Wawrzesta
Height:	2 ¾", 7.0 cm
Colour:	Brown kitten; blue suit; white collar; yellow straw hat
Issued:	June 1997-Dec. 1999

PRICING DATA	U.K. £	U.S. $	Can. $
Made Abroad	15.00	25.00	35.00

AGE 4 (LITTLE RABBITS)™

TECHNICAL DATA

Model No.:	269476
Modeller:	Richard Wawrzesta
Height:	3", 7.6 cm
Colour:	Brown rabbits; blue jacket; red handkerchief
Issued:	June 1997-Dec. 1999

PRICING DATA	U.K. £	U.S. $	Can. $
Made Abroad	15.00	25.00	35.00

AGE 5 (MENDING MICE)™

TECHNICAL DATA

Model No.:	269484
Modeller:	Richard Wawrzesta
Height:	2 ½", 6.4 cm
Colour:	Brown mouse; white cloth with blue and red designs; white candle; gold candleholder
Issued:	June 1997-Dec. 1999

PRICING DATA	U.K. £	U.S. $	Can. $
Made Abroad	15.00	25.00	35.00

FIGURINES
GROWING UP

AGE 6 (SLEEPING BUNNIES)™

TECHNICAL DATA

Model No.:	269492
Modeller:	Richard Wawrzesta
Height:	2 ½", 6.4 cm
Colour:	Brown bunny; green foliage
Issued:	June 1997-Dec. 1999

PRICING DATA	U.K. £	U.S. $	Can. $
Made Abroad	15.00	25.00	35.00

FIGURINES
STORYBOOK

THE TALE OF A FIERCE BAD RABBIT™

TECHNICAL DATA

Model No.:	545945
Modeller:	Richard Wawrzesta
Height:	3 ½", 8.9 cm
Colour:	Brown rabbit; blue-grey bench
Issued:	Jan. 1999 to the present

PRICING DATA	U.K. £	U.S. $	Can. $
Made Abroad	12.95	—	—

THE TALE OF BENJAMIN BUNNY™

TECHNICAL DATA

Model No.:	BPM53/199540
Modeller:	Richard Wawrzesta
Height:	3 ½", 8.9 cm
Colour:	Brown rabbit and jacket; black tam with red pompon
Issued:	Jan. 1995 to the present

PRICING DATA	U.K. £	U.S. $	Can. $
Made in U.K.	25.00	40.00	60.00
Made Abroad	12.95	—	—

THE TALE OF GINGER AND PICKLES™

TECHNICAL DATA

Model No.:	545929
Modeller:	Richard Wawrzesta
Height:	2 ¾", 7.0 cm
Colour:	Brown rabbit; blue coat; tan basket; green windowframe; red brick
Issued:	Jan. 1999 to the present

PRICING DATA	U.K. £	U.S. $	Can. $
Made Abroad	12.95	—	—

FIGURINES
STORYBOOK

THE TALE OF JEMIMA PUDDLE-DUCK™

TECHNICAL DATA

Model No.:	BPM58/268674
Modeller:	Richard Wawrzesta
Height:	3 ½", 8.9 cm
Colour:	White duck; blue bonnet; pink and blue shawl
Issued:	Jan. 1996 to the present

PRICING DATA	U.K. £	U.S. $	Can. $
Made in U.K.	25.00	40.00	60.00
Made Abroad	12.95	—	—

THE TALE OF JOHNNY TOWN-MOUSE™

TECHNICAL DATA

Model No.:	467553
Modeller:	Richard Wawrzesta
Height:	3", 7.6 cm
Colour:	Brown mouse, coat and hat; yellow waistcoat; tan briefcase
Issued:	Jan. 1998 to the present

PRICING DATA	U.K. £	U.S. $	Can. $
Made Abroad	12.95	—	—

THE TALE OF LITTLE PIG ROBINSON™

TECHNICAL DATA

Model No.:	545937
Modeller:	Richard Wawrzesta
Height:	3", 7.6 cm
Colour:	Pink pig; blue and white striped outfit; rose-pink chair; tan telescope
Issued:	Jan. 1999 to the present

PRICING DATA	U.K. £	U.S. $	Can. $
Made Abroad	12.95	—	—

FIGURINES
STORYBOOK

THE TALE OF MR. JEREMY FISHER™

TECHNICAL DATA

Model No.:	BPM56/199486
Modeller:	Richard Wawrzesta
Height:	2 ¾", 7.0 cm
Colour:	Greenish-yellow frog; white coat; brown pack; blue books
Issued:	Jan. 1996 to the present

PRICING DATA	U.K. £	U.S. $	Can. $
Made in U.K.	25.00	40.00	60.00
Made Abroad	12.95	—	—

THE TALE OF MR. TOD ™

TECHNICAL DATA

Model No.:	467561
Modeller:	Richard Wawrzesta
Height:	3 ½", 8.9 cm
Colour:	Reddish-brown fox; brown coat, trousers and fencing; red waistcoat
Issued:	Jan. 1998 to the present

PRICING DATA	U.K. £	U.S. $	Can. $
Made Abroad	12.95	—	—

THE TALE OF MRS. TIGGY-WINKLE™

TECHNICAL DATA

Model No.:	BPM55/199559
Modeller:	Richard Wawrzesta
Height:	3", 7.6 cm
Colour:	Dark and light brown hedgehog; white, pink, yellow and blue clothing
Issued:	Jan. 1995 to the present

PRICING DATA	U.K. £	U.S. $	Can. $
Made in U.K.	25.00	40.00	60.00
Made Abroad	12.95	—	—

FIGURINES
STORYBOOK

THE TALE OF MRS. TITTLEMOUSE™

TECHNICAL DATA

Model No.:	BPM60/268682
Modeller:	Richard Wawrzesta
Height:	3", 7. 6 cm
Colour:	Brown mouse; white, pale blue and red clothing
Issued:	Jan. 1996-Dec. 1998

PRICING DATA	U.K. £	U.S. $	Can. $
Made in U.K.	25.00	40.00	60.00
Made Abroad	15.00	25.00	35.00

THE TALE OF PETER RABBIT™

TECHNICAL DATA

Model No.:	BPM50/199443
Modeller:	Richard Wawrzesta
Height:	3 ½", 8.9 cm
Colour:	Brown rabbit; blue jacket
Issued:	Jan. 1995 to the present

PRICING DATA	U.K. £	U.S. $	Can. $
Made in U.K.	25.00	40.00	60.00
Made Abroad	12.95	—	—

THE TALE OF PIE AND THE PATTY PAN™

TECHNICAL DATA

Model No.:	545910
Modeller:	Richard Wawrzesta
Height:	3 ¼", 8.3 cm
Colour:	Black dog; red, blue, yellow and green bouquet
Issued:	Jan. 1999 to the present

PRICING DATA	U.K. £	U.S. $	Can. $
Made Abroad	12.95	—	—

FIGURINES
STORYBOOK

THE TALE OF PIGLING BLAND™

TECHNICAL DATA

Model No.:	467545
Modeller:	Richard Wawrzesta
Height:	3 ½", 8.9 cm
Colour:	Pink pig; lilac coat; blue and white striped waistcoat; red handkerchief; tan stick
Issued:	Jan. 1998 to the present

PRICING DATA	U.K. £	U.S. $	Can. $
Made Abroad	12.95	—	—

THE TALE OF SAMUEL WHISKERS™

TECHNICAL DATA

Model No.:	467537
Modeller:	Richard Wawrzesta
Height:	2 ½", 6.4 cm
Colour:	Brown mouse; green coat; yellow waistcoat; brown pantaloons
Issued:	Jan. 1998 to the present

PRICING DATA	U.K. £	U.S. $	Can. $
Made Abroad	12.95	—	—

THE TALE OF SQUIRREL NUTKIN™

TECHNICAL DATA

Model No.:	BPM51/199494
Modeller:	Richard Wawrzesta
Height:	3 ½", 8.9 cm
Colour:	Reddish-brown and white squirrel
Issued:	Jan. 1995-Dec. 1998

PRICING DATA	U.K. £	U.S. $	Can. $
Made in U.K.	25.00	40.00	60.00
Made Abroad	12.95	—	—

FIGURINES
STORYBOOK

THE TALE OF THE FLOPSY BUNNIES™

TECHNICAL DATA

Model No.:	BPM59/268704
Modeller:	Richard Wawrzesta
Height:	3 ¼", 8.3 cm
Colour:	Brown rabbits; salmon jacket; blue frock
Issued:	Jan. 1996 to the present

PRICING DATA	U.K. £	U.S. $	Can. $
Made in U.K.	25.00	40.00	60.00
Made Abroad	12.95	—	—

THE TALE OF THE TAILOR OF GLOUCESTER™

TECHNICAL DATA

Model No.:	BPM52/199532
Modeller:	Richard Wawrzesta
Height:	3 ½", 8.9 cm
Colour:	Brown mouse; tan spool of fuchsia thread
Issued:	Jan. 1995 to the present

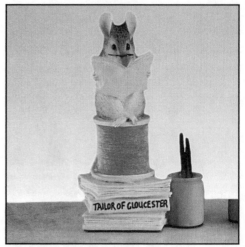

PRICING DATA	U.K. £	U.S. $	Can. $
Made in U.K.	25.00	40.00	60.00
Made Abroad	12.95	—	—

THE TALE OF TIMMY TIPTOES™

TECHNICAL DATA

Model No.:	BPM61/268690
Modeller:	Richard Wawrzesta
Height:	3 ¼", 8.3 cm
Colour:	Brown, white and pink squirrel; salmon jacket
Issued:	Jan. 1996-Dec. 1998

PRICING DATA	U.K. £	U.S. $	Can. $
Made in U.K.	25.00	40.00	60.00
Made Abroad	15.00	25.00	35.00

FIGURINES
STORYBOOK

THE TALE OF TOM KITTEN™

TECHNICAL DATA

Model No.:	BPM57/199478
Modeller:	Richard Wawrzesta
Height:	3 ¼", 8.3 cm
Colour:	Ginger tabby cat; blue suit
Issued:	Jan. 1996 to the present

PRICING DATA	U.K. £	U.S. $	Can. $
Made in U.K.	25.00	40.00	60.00
Made Abroad	12.95	—	—

THE TALE OF TWO BAD MICE™

TECHNICAL DATA

Model No.:	BPM54/199516
Modeller:	Richard Wawrzesta
Height:	3", 7.6 cm
Colour:	Brown mouse; lilac and white clothing
Issued:	Jan. 1995 to the present
Varieties:	1. Base - "Hunca Munca" 2. Base - "The Tale of Two Bad Mice"

PRICING DATA	U.K. £	U.S. $	Can. $
Made in U.K.	25.00	40.00	60.00
Made Abroad	12.95	—	—

BOOKENDS

"GOOD LITTLE BUNNIES AND NAUGHTY PETER RABBIT"™

TECHNICAL DATA

Model No.:	BPA20/282693
Modeller:	Richard Wawrzesta
Size:	5 ¾" x 12", 14.0 x 30.5 cm
Colour:	Left: Three brown rabbits picking blackberries
	Right: Peter Rabbit eating radishes
Issued:	Jan. 1994-Dec. 1999

PRICING DATA	U.K. £	U.S. $	Can. $
Made in U.K.	75.00	125.00	165.00
Made Abroad	60.00	95.00	150.00

Note: Prices refer to the pair of bookends.

"NOW RUN ALONG, AND DON'T GET INTO MISCHIEF"™

TECHNICAL DATA

Model No.:	BPA19/282685
Modeller:	Richard Wawrzesta
Size:	5 ¾" x 11", 14.6 x 27.9 cm
Colour:	Left: Mrs. Rabbit and Peter: blue, white and brown
	Right: Flopsy, Mopsy and Cotton-tail: brown and pink
Issued:	Jan. 1994-Dec. 1999

PRICING DATA	U.K. £	U.S. $	Can. $
Made in U.K.	75.00	125.00	165.00
Made Abroad	60.00	95.00	150.00

Note: Prices refer to the pair of bookends.

CAMEOS

AUNT PETTITOES™

TECHNICAL DATA

Model No.:	CM9
Modeller:	Richard Wawrzesta
Height:	8", 20.3 cm
Colour:	Pink pigs; blue, white and grey clothing; grey pails; cream farmhouse; grey fence
Issued:	Jan. 1992-Dec. 1994

PRICING DATA	U.K. £	U.S. $	Can. $
Made in U.K.	30.00	50.00	70.00

FOXY WHISKERED GENTLEMAN™

TECHNICAL DATA

Model No.:	CM5
Modeller:	Richard Wawrzesta
Height:	8", 20.3 cm
Colour:	Reddish-white fox; pink waistcoat and foxgloves; cream pantaloons; green jacket; grey fence
Issued:	July 1990-Dec. 1993

PRICING DATA	U.K. £	U.S. $	Can. $
Made in U.K.	30.00	50.00	70.00

HUNCA MUNCA AND THE BABIES™

TECHNICAL DATA

Model No.:	CM10
Modeller:	Richard Wawrzesta
Height:	6", 15.0 cm
Colour:	Brown mice with pink ears; blue and white clothing; pink blanket; tan cradle and floor; brown dresser
Issued:	Jan. 1992-Dec. 1994

PRICING DATA	U.K. £	U.S. $	Can. $
Made in U.K.	30.00	50.00	70.00

CAMEOS

JEMIMA PUDDLE-DUCK MEETS HENNY PENNY™

TECHNICAL DATA

Model No.:	CM3
Modeller:	Richard Wawrzesta
Height:	6", 15.0 cm
Colour:	Jemima: white duck; rose-pink and blue clothing Henny Penny: yellow hen and chicks; green clothing
Issued:	Jan. 1989-Dec. 1993

PRICING DATA	U.K. £	U.S. $	Can. $
Made in U.K.	30.00	50.00	70.00

JEREMY FISHER™

TECHNICAL DATA

Model No.:	CM2
Modeller:	Richard Wawrzesta
Height:	8", 20.3 cm
Colour:	Yellowish-green frog; pink waistcoat; white newspaper; silver fish; cream window
Issued:	Jan. 1989-Dec. 1993

PRICING DATA	U.K. £	U.S. $	Can. $
Made in U.K.	30.00	50.00	70.00

OLD WOMAN WHO LIVED IN A SHOE™

TECHNICAL DATA

Model No.:	CM7
Modeller:	Richard Wawrzesta
Size:	6" x 8", 15.0 x 20.3 cm
Colour:	Brown mice with pink ears and tails; white clothing; blue shoe with white lace trim; lilac background
Issued:	July 1990-Dec. 1994

PRICING DATA	U.K. £	U.S. $	Can. $
Made in U.K.	30.00	50.00	70.00

CAMEOS

PETER RABBIT™

TECHNICAL DATA

Model No.:	CM1
Modeller:	Richard Wawrzesta
Height:	8", 20.3 cm
Colour:	Brown and white rabbit; blue jacket; red robin; brown spade; red radishes
Issued:	Jan. 1989-Dec. 1994

PRICING DATA	U.K. £	U.S. $	Can. $
Made in U.K.	30.00	50.00	70.00

TAILOR OF GLOUCESTER™

TECHNICAL DATA

Model No.:	CM8
Modeller:	Richard Wawrzesta
Height:	8", 20.3 cm
Colour:	Brown mouse; white paper; tan spool with fuchsia thread; grey thimble
Issued:	July 1990-Dec. 1994

PRICING DATA	U.K. £	U.S. $	Can. $
Made in U.K.	30.00	50.00	70.00

THIS ONE IS MOPPET™

TECHNICAL DATA

Model No.:	CM4
Modeller:	Richard Wawrzesta
Size:	6" x 8", 15.0 x 20.3 cm
Colour:	White cat; violet frock; white apron; ginger and grey tabby kittens; brown dresser
Issued:	Jan. 1989-Dec. 1994

PRICING DATA	U.K. £	U.S. $	Can. $
Made in U.K.	30.00	50.00	70.00

CAMEOS

TIMMY WILLIE AND THE STRAWBERRY™

TECHNICAL DATA

Model No.:	CM6
Modeller:	Richard Wawrzesta
Size:	6" x 8", 15.0 x 20.3 cm
Colour:	Brown mouse; red strawberries; green leaves
Issued:	July 1990-Dec. 1993

PRICING DATA	U.K. £	U.S. $	Can. $
Made in U.K.	30.00	50.00	70.00

CLOCKS

JEMIMA PUDDLE-DUCK AND DUCKLINGS™

TECHNICAL DATA

Model No.:	472247
Modeller:	Richard Wawrzesta
Height:	5", 12.7 cm
Colour:	White duck: blue bonnet; rose and blue shawl; yellow ducklings; flowered clock
Issued:	Jan. 1999-Dec. 1999

PRICING DATA	U.K. £	U.S. $	Can. $
Made Abroad	30.00	50.00	70.00

Note: European exclusive.

JEMIMA PUDDLE-DUCK AND THE FOXY WHISKERED GENTLEMAN™

TECHNICAL DATA

Model No.:	BP38
Modeller:	Richard Wawrzesta
Height:	3", 7.6 cm
Colour:	White duck: blue bonnet; rose and blue shawl; reddish-brown fox: green jacket; red waistcoat
Issued:	Jan. 1996-Dec. 1998

PRICING DATA	U.K. £	U.S. $	Can. $
Made Abroad	30.00	50.00	70.00

MR. JEREMY FISHER™

TECHNICAL DATA

Model No.:	BP37
Modeller:	Richard Wawrzesta
Height:	3", 7.6 cm
Colour:	Yellow and brown frog; white jacket; tan and green clock
Issued:	Jan. 1996-Dec. 1998

PRICING DATA	U.K. £	U.S. $	Can. $
Made Abroad	30.00	50.00	70.00

CLOCKS

MRS. RABBIT™

TECHNICAL DATA

Model No.:	269654
Modeller:	Richard Wawrzesta
Height:	7 ¼", 18.4 cm
Colour:	Mrs. Rabbit: brown; blue dress; white apron Rabbits: brown; red jackets Peter: brown; blue jacket
Medium:	Ceramic
Issued:	Jan. 1999 to the present
Series:	Nursery Collection

PRICING DATA	U.K. £	U.S. $	Can. $
Made Abroad	24.95	—	—

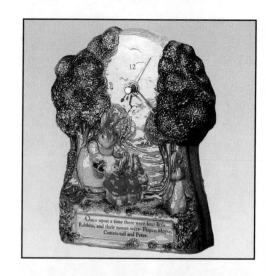

MRS. RABBIT, PETER, FLOPSY, MOPSY AND COTTON-TAIL™

TECHNICAL DATA

Model No.:	BP35/284025
Modeller:	Richard Wawrzesta
Height:	3", 7.6 cm
Colour:	Tan clock; brown rabbits; blue, white and salmon clothing
Issued:	Jan. 1996-Dec. 1999

PRICING DATA	U.K. £	U.S. $	Can. $
Made Abroad	30.00	50.00	70.00

MRS. TIGGY-WINKLE™

TECHNICAL DATA

Model No.:	BP31
Modeller:	Richard Wawrzesta
Height:	5 ½", 14.0 cm
Colour:	Brown hedgehog; pink, white, red and blue clothing
Issued:	July 1992-Dec. 1996

PRICING DATA	U.K. £	U.S. $	Can. $
Made in U.K.	50.00	75.00	95.00

CLOCKS

PETER RABBIT™

TECHNICAL DATA

Model No.:	BP30
Modeller:	Richard Wawrzesta
Height:	6", 15.0 cm
Colour:	Brown rabbit, basket, spade and clock; blue jacket; pot of pink flowers
Issued:	July 1992-Dec. 1996

PRICING DATA	U.K. £	U.S. $	Can. $
Made in U.K.	50.00	75.00	95.00

PETER RABBIT IN THE GARDEN™

TECHNICAL DATA

Model No.:	BP34/284289
Modeller:	Richard Wawrzesta
Height:	6 ¼", 15.9 cm
Colour:	Tan clock; brown rabbit; blue coat; robin seated on brown spade handle; green leaves
Issued:	Jan. 1995-Dec. 1999

PRICING DATA	U.K. £	U.S. $	Can. $
Made Abroad	40.00	65.00	85.00

PETER RABBIT WITH BOOK™

TECHNICAL DATA

Model No.:	CBP02
Modeller:	Richard Wawrzesta
Height:	6 ½", 16.5 cm
Colour:	Brown rabbit; blue jacket; green book/clock
Issued:	Jan. 1993 in a limited edition of 1,993
Series:	100th Anniversary of Peter Rabbit (1893-1993)

PRICING DATA	U.K. £	U.S. $	Can. $
Made in U.K.	75.00	125.00	165.00

CLOCKS

THE TAILOR OF GLOUCESTER™

TECHNICAL DATA

Model No.:	BP36/284068
Modeller:	Richard Wawrzesta
Height:	3", 7.6 cm
Colour:	Tan clock; brown mice; fuchsia and violet clothing
Issued:	Jan. 1996-June 1999

PRICING DATA	U.K. £	U.S. $	Can. $
Made Abroad	30.00	50.00	70.00

MONEY BANKS

BENJAMIN BUNNY™

TECHNICAL DATA

Model No.: 484202
Modeller: Richard Wawrzesta
Height: 6 ¾", 17.2 cm
Colour: Brown rabbit; yellow jacket; red handkerchief; green tam with red pompon
Medium: Ceramic
Issued: Jan. 1999 to the present

PRICING DATA	U.K. £	U.S. $	Can. $
Made Abroad	14.95	—	—

FOXY WHISKERED GENTLEMAN™

TECHNICAL DATA

Model No.: 471887
Modeller: Richard Wawrzesta
Height: 7 ¾", 19.7 cm
Colour: Reddish-brown; green coat and trousers; red waistcoat
Medium: Ceramic
Issued: Jan. 1999 to the present

PRICING DATA	U.K. £	U.S. $	Can. $
Made Abroad	14.95	—	—

JEMIMA PUDDLE-DUCK™

TECHNICAL DATA

Model No.: 471879
Modeller: Richard Wawrzesta
Height: 7 ¾", 19.7 cm
Colour: White duck; rose-pink and blue shawl; blue bonnet
Medium: Ceramic
Issued: Jan. 1999 to the present

PRICING DATA	U.K. £	U.S. $	Can. $
Made Abroad	14.95	—	—

MONEY BANKS

MR. JEREMY FISHER™
Style One

TECHNICAL DATA

Model No.:	BPMB05/282855
Modeller:	Richard Wawrzesta
Height:	4 ¼", 10.8 cm
Colour:	Green frog; rose jacket; brown basket; white paper
Medium:	Resin
Issued:	1995 to the present

PRICING DATA	U.K. £	U.S. $	Can. $
Made Abroad	22.95	—	—

MR. JEREMY FISHER™
Style Two

TECHNICAL DATA

Model No.:	484210
Modeller:	Richard Wawrzesta
Height:	6", 15.0 cm
Colour:	Green frog; rose jacket; black shoes; brown box
Medium:	Ceramic
Issued:	June 1999 to the present

PRICING DATA	U.K. £	U.S. $	Can. $
Made Abroad	14.95	—	—

MRS. RABBIT AND PETER™

TECHNICAL DATA

Model No.:	BPMB02
Modeller:	Richard Wawrzesta
Height:	6 ¼", 15.9 cm
Colour:	Mrs Rabbit: blue dress; white apron and bowl; green headboard; white bedding; pink and white ruffle
Medium:	Resin
Issued:	Jan. 1995-Dec. 1998

PRICING DATA	U.K. £	U.S. $	Can. $
Made Abroad	25.00	40.00	60.00

MONEY BANKS

MRS. RABBIT WITH BABIES™

TECHNICAL DATA

Model No.:	269603
Modeller:	Richard Wawrzesta
Height:	7 ¾", 19.7 cm
Colour:	Brown rabbits; blue dress; white apron; green chair
Issued:	Jan. 1998 to the present
Medium:	Ceramic
Series:	Nursery Collection

PRICING DATA	U.K. £	U.S. $	Can. $
Made Abroad	14.95	—	—

MRS. TIGGY-WINKLE™

TECHNICAL DATA

Model No.:	484199
Modeller:	Richard Wawrzesta
Height:	6", 15.0 cm
Colour:	Brown hedgehog; rose blouse; yellow and blue striped skirt; white cap
Medium:	Ceramic
Issued:	Jan. 1999 to the present

PRICING DATA	U.K. £	U.S. $	Can. $
Made Abroad	14.95	—	—

OLD WOMAN WHO LIVED IN A SHOE™

TECHNICAL DATA

Model No.:	BPMB01/282812
Modeller:	Richard Wawrzesta
Height:	5 ½", 14.0 cm
Colour:	Pale blue shoe with white lace; brown mice with pink ears; cream bonnet with pink bow
Medium:	Resin
Issued:	Jan. 1995 to the present

PRICING DATA	U.K. £	U.S. $	Can. $
Made Abroad	22.95	—	—

MONEY BANKS

PETER RABBIT IN WATERING CAN™

TECHNICAL DATA

Model No.:	BPM06/282863
Modeller:	Richard Wawrzesta
Height:	6 ¾", 17.2 cm
Colour:	Brown rabbit; pale green watering can
Medium:	Resin
Issued:	1995 to the present

PRICING DATA	U.K. £	U.S. $	Can. $
Made Abroad	22.95	—	—

PETER RABBIT WITH ONIONS™

TECHNICAL DATA

Model No.:	BPMB03/282839
Modeller:	Richard Wawrzesta
Height:	7", 17.8 cm
Colour:	Brown rabbit; blue jacket; red and white handkerchief; brown onions
Medium:	Resin
Issued:	Jan. 1995 to the present

PRICING DATA	U.K. £	U.S. $	Can. $
Made Abroad	22.95	—	—

MONEY BANKS

PIGLING BLAND™

TECHNICAL DATA

Model No.:	BPMB04/282847
Modeller:	Richard Wawrzesta
Height:	7", 17.8 cm
Colour:	Pink pig; reddish-brown coat; tan trousers; white and blue striped waistcoat; white bowl
Medium:	Resin
Issued:	Jan. 1995-Dec. 1998

PRICING DATA	U.K. £	U.S. $	Can. $
Made Abroad	25.00	40.00	60.00

THE TAILOR OF GLOUCESTER™

TECHNICAL DATA

Model No.:	620300
Modeller:	Richard Wawrzesta
Height:	6 ¾", 17.2 cm
Colour:	Brown and white mouse; tan spool of fuchsia thread; white paper
Medium:	Ceramic
Issued:	June 1999 to the present

PRICING DATA	U.K. £	U.S. $	Can. $
Made Abroad	14.95	—	—

MUSICALS

BENJAMIN BUNNY™

TECHNICAL DATA

Model No.:	297712
Modeller:	Richard Wawrzesta
Height:	4 ¾", 12.1 cm
Colour:	Brown rabbit; green tam with red pompon; red handkerchief
Issued:	June 1999 to the present
Tune:	Mozart's "Lullaby"
Medium:	Ceramic
Series:	Storybook Musicals

PRICING DATA	U.K. £	U.S. $	Can. $
Made Abroad	19.95	—	—

FOXY WHISKERED GENTLEMAN™

TECHNICAL DATA

Model No.:	297704
Modeller:	Richard Wawrzesta
Height:	4 ¾", 12.1 cm
Colour:	Brown fox, shoes and stump; green jacket and pantaloons
Issued:	June 1997 to the present
Tune:	"Oh What A Beautiful Morning"
Medium:	Ceramic
Series:	Storybook Musicals

PRICING DATA	U.K. £	U.S. $	Can. $
Made Abroad	19.95	—	—

HUNCA MUNCA™
Style One

TECHNICAL DATA

Model No.:	297720
Modeller:	Richard Wawrzesta
Height:	4 ¼", 10.8 cm
Colour:	Brown mice; blue dress with white trim; tan chair; cream blanket
Issued:	June 1997 to the present
Tune:	Brahm's "Lullaby"
Medium:	Ceramic
Series:	Storybook Musicals

PRICING DATA	U.K. £	U.S. $	Can. $
Made Abroad	19.95	—	—

MUSICALS

HUNCA MUNCA™
Style Two

TECHNICAL DATA

Model No.: 508802
Modeller: Richard Wawrzesta
Height: 4 ¾", 12.1 cm
Colour: Brown, lilac, white, blue and yellow
Issued: June 1999 to the present
Tune: "Swan Lake"
Medium: Resin
Series: Miniature Musicals

PRICING DATA	U.K. £	U.S. $	Can. $
Made Abroad	19.95	—	—

JEMIMA PUDDLE-DUCK™
Style One

TECHNICAL DATA

Model No.: 199591
Modeller: Richard Wawrzesta
Height: 6", 15.0 cm
Colour: White, rose-pink and blue
Issued: June 1996 to the present
Tune: "Oh What A Beautiful Morning"
Medium: Ceramic
Series: Musicals

PRICING DATA	U.K. £	U.S. $	Can. $
Made Abroad	29.95	—	—

JEMIMA PUDDLE-DUCK™
Style Two

TECHNICAL DATA

Model No.: 508829
Modeller: Richard Wawrzesta
Height: 5", 12.7 cm
Colour: White, rose-pink, blue and green
Issued: June 1999 to the present
Tune: "Au Clair de la Lune"
Medium: Resin
Series: Miniature Musicals

PRICING DATA	U.K. £	U.S. $	Can. $
Made Abroad	19.95	—	—

MUSICALS

MISS MOPPET™

TECHNICAL DATA

Model No.:	297739
Modeller:	Richard Wawrzesta
Height:	4 ¾", 12.1 cm
Colour:	Brown kitten; blue handkerchief; red suitcase; blue books
Issued:	June 1997 to the present
Tune:	Schubert's "Lullaby"
Medium:	Ceramic
Series:	Storybook Musicals

PRICING DATA	U.K. £	U.S. $	Can. $
Made Abroad	19.95	—	—

MISS MOPPET

MR. JEREMY FISHER™

TECHNICAL DATA

Model No.:	199621
Modeller:	Richard Wawrzesta
Height:	4 ½", 11.9 cm
Colour:	Yellow-green frog; white jacket; grey pail and fish; white lily
Issued:	June 1996 to the present
Tune:	"Waltz of the Flowers"
Medium:	Ceramic
Series:	Musicals

PRICING DATA	U.K. £	U.S. $	Can. $
Made Abroad	29.95	—	—

MRS. RABBIT WITH BUNNIES™

TECHNICAL DATA

Model No.:	269646
Modeller:	Richard Wawrzesta
Height:	6 ¼", 15.9 cm
Colour:	Brown rabbits; white, blue and red clothing; yellow base
Issued:	1998 to the present
Tune:	"Au Clair de la Lune"
Medium:	Ceramic
Series:	Nursery Collection

PRICING DATA	U.K. £	U.S. $	Can. $
Made Abroad	29.95	—	—

MUSICALS

MRS. TIGGY-WINKLE™
Style One

TECHNICAL DATA

Model No.:	199605
Modeller:	Richard Wawrzesta
Height:	5 ¼", 13.3 cm
Colour:	Brown, pink and white
Issued:	June 1996 to the present
Tune:	"In the Garden"
Medium:	Ceramic
Series:	Musicals

PRICING DATA	U.K. £	U.S. $	Can. $
Made Abroad	29.95	—	—

MRS. TIGGY-WINKLE™
Style Two

TECHNICAL DATA

Model No.:	297690
Modeller:	Richard Wawrzesta
Height:	4 ¼", 10.8 cm
Colour:	Brown, white, red and yellow
Issued:	June 1997 to the present
Tune:	"Au Clair de la Lune"
Medium:	Ceramic
Series:	Storybook Musicals

PRICING DATA	U.K. £	U.S. $	Can. $
Made Abroad	19.95	—	—

MRS. TIGGY-WINKLE™
Style Three

TECHNICAL DATA

Model No.:	508810
Modeller:	Richard Wawrzesta
Height:	4 ¾", 12.1 cm
Colour:	Brown, rose-pink, white and tan
Issued:	June 1999 to the present
Tune:	"Waltz of the Flowers"
Medium:	Resin
Series:	Miniature Musicals

PRICING DATA	U.K. £	U.S. $	Can. $
Made Abroad	19.95	—	—

MUSICALS

PETER RABBIT™
Style One

TECHNICAL DATA

Model No.:	199583
Modeller:	Richard Wawrzesta
Height:	7", 17.8 cm
Colour:	Brown, blue, red, tan and brown
Issued:	June 1996 to the present
Tune:	Schubert's "Lullaby"
Medium:	Ceramic
Series:	Musicals

PRICING DATA	U.K. £	U.S. $	Can. $
Made Abroad	29.95	—	—

PETER RABBIT™
Style Two

TECHNICAL DATA

Model No.:	297747
Modeller:	Richard Wawrzesta
Height:	5", 12.7 cm
Colour:	Brown, blue and red
Issued:	June 1997 to the present
Tune:	"In the Garden"
Medium:	Ceramic
Series:	Storybook Musicals

PRICING DATA	U.K. £	U.S. $	Can. $
Made Abroad	19.95	—	—

PETER RABBIT™
Style Three

TECHNICAL DATA

Model No.:	508799
Modeller:	Richard Wawrzesta
Height:	5 ¼", 13.3 cm
Colour:	Brown, blue, red and green
Issued:	June 1999 to the present
Tune:	"Autumn Leaves"
Medium:	Resin
Series:	Miniature Musicals

PRICING DATA	U.K. £	U.S. $	Can. $
Made Abroad	19.95	—	—

PETER PAN™

Peter Pan

Wendy

Tinker Bell

Smee

BEATRIX POTTER™

Cousin Ribby

Miss Moppet And The Mouse

Tailor Of Gloucester, Style One

Cecily Parsley Ran Away

BEATRIX POTTER™

Peter Rabbit In The Garden, Style One

Timmy Willie And The Strawberry

The Amiable Guinea Pig

Nutkin Tickling Old Mr. Brown

BEATRIX POTTER™

Old Mr. Bunny

Peter Rabbit Eating A Radish

Peter Rabbit, Jemima Puddle-duck, and Mrs. Tiggy-Winkle Trinket Boxes

BEATRIX POTTER™

Lady Mouse

Tom Kitten With Butterfly

Benjamin Bunny

Foxy Whiskered Gentleman, Style One

BEATRIX POTTER™

Hunca Munca Sweeping, Style One

Mrs. Rabbit At Work

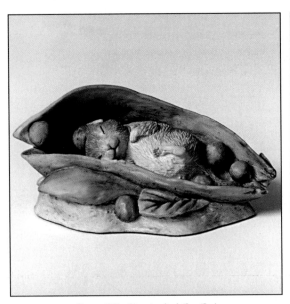

Timmy Willie Sleeping In A Pea Pod

This One Is Moppet

WINNIE THE POOH™

Tigger,™ Pooh™ And Piglet™

Pooh™ And Mirror

Pooh,™ Eeyore™ And Hunny

Pooh,™ Piglet™ And Flowers

RUFF & REDDY™

Taking The Biscuit

If The Cap Fits

Not My Size

Scarecrow Scallywags

MUSICALS

RABBIT SHOVELLING SNOW™

TECHNICAL DATA

Model No.:	361690
Modeller:	Richard Wawrzesta
Height:	7 ¼", 18.4 cm
Colour:	Brown rabbit and fence; red jacket and scarf; brown and grey shovel
Issued:	June 1998-Dec. 1999
Tune:	"The First Noël"
Medium:	Ceramic
Series:	Musicals

PRICING DATA	U.K. £	U.S. $	Can. $
Made Abroad	30.00	50.00	75.00

RABBIT WITH STICKS™

TECHNICAL DATA

Model No.:	361666
Modeller:	Richard Wawrzesta
Height:	7 ¼", 18.4 cm
Colour:	Brown rabbit and bundle of sticks; red jacket
Issued:	June 1998-Dec. 1999
Tune:	"The First Noël"
Medium:	Ceramic
Series:	Musicals

PRICING DATA	U.K. £	U.S. $	Can. $
Made Abroad	30.00	50.00	75.00

THE TAILOR OF GLOUCESTER™

TECHNICAL DATA

Model No.:	199648
Modeller:	Richard Wawrzesta
Height:	5 ¼", 13.3 cm
Colour:	Brown mouse; blue and white cloth; silver thimble; fuchsia thread
Issued:	June 1996-Dec. 1999
Tune:	Brahm's "Lullaby"
Medium:	Ceramic
Series:	Musicals

PRICING DATA	U.K. £	U.S. $	Can. $
Made Abroad	30.00	50.00	75.00

MUSICALS

TOM KITTEN™

TECHNICAL DATA

Model No.:	199613
Modeller:	Richard Wawrzesta
Height:	7", 17.8 cm
Colour:	Brown kitten; blue outfit; tan straw hat; green foliage with white and pink flowers; orange butterfly
Issued:	June 1996 to the present
Tune:	"Au Clair de la Lune"
Medium:	Ceramic
Series:	Musicals

PRICING DATA	U.K. £	U.S. $	Can. $
Made Abroad	29.95	—	—

TWO RABBITS IN WINTER™

TECHNICAL DATA

Model No.:	361682
Modeller:	Richard Wawrzesta
Height:	6 ¾", 17.2 cm
Colour:	Brown rabbits; brown jacket; red cloak; tan basket; blue umbrella
Issued:	June 1998-Dec. 1999
Tune:	"We Wish You a Merry Christmas"
Medium:	Ceramic
Series:	Musicals

PRICING DATA	U.K. £	U.S. $	Can. $
Made Abroad	30.00	50.00	75.00

POINT OF SALE DISPLAYS

These point of sale displays were not originally available for sale to the general public.

THE TAILOR OF GLOUCESTER™

TECHNICAL DATA

Model No.:	DISP8
Designer:	Unknown
Height:	4 ½", 11.9 cm
Colour:	Brown, cream, fuchsia and white
Issued:	Unknown

PRICING DATA	U.K. £	U.S. $	Can. $
Made in U.K.	10.00	15.00	25.00

Note: Display does not include figurines.

THE TALE OF GINGER AND PICKLES™

TECHNICAL DATA

Model No.:	DISP7
Designer:	Unknown
Height:	4 ½", 11.9 cm
Colour:	Cream and brown
Issued:	Unknown

PRICING DATA	U.K. £	U.S. $	Can. $
Made in U.K.	10.00	15.00	25.00

Note: Display does not include figurines.

THE TALE OF JEMIMA PUDDLE-DUCK™

TECHNICAL DATA

Model No.:	DISP6
Designer:	Unknown
Height:	4 ½", 11.9 cm
Colour:	White, tan, brown and light pink tones
Issued:	Unknown

PRICING DATA	U.K. £	U.S. $	Can. $
Made in U.K.	10.00	15.00	25.00

Note: Display does not include figurines.

POINT OF SALE DISPLAYS

THE TALE OF PETER RABBIT™

TECHNICAL DATA

Model No.: DISP5
Designer: Unknown
Height: 4 ½", 11.9 cm
Colour: Brown, tan and light blue tones
Issued: Unknown

PRICING DATA	U.K. £	U.S. $	Can. $
Made in U.K.	10.00	15.00	25.00

Note: Display does not include figurines.

THE TALE OF TWO BAD MICE™

TECHNICAL DATA

Model No.: DISP9
Designer: Unknown
Height: 4 ½", 11.9 cm
Colour: Cream, yellow and brown
Issued: Unknown

PRICING DATA	U.K. £	U.S. $	Can. $
Made in U.K.	10.00	15.00	25.00

Note: Display does not include figurines.

THE WORLD OF BEATRIX POTTER DISPLAY™

TECHNICAL DATA

Model No.: SPE811
Designer: Unknown
Size: 15" x 11" x 3 ½",
38.1 x 27.9 x 8.9 cm
Colour: Top shelf: peach and pink
Middle shelf: blue and pink
Bottom shelf: peach, pink and red
Issued: 1997

PRICING DATA	U.K. £	U.S. $	Can. $
Made in U.K.	15.00	25.00	35.00

Note: Display does not include figurines.

TRINKET BOXES

JEMIMA PUDDLE-DUCK™

TECHNICAL DATA

Model No.: CBP06
Modeller: Richard Wawrzesta
Height: 3 ¾", 9.5 cm
Colour: Cream and green box;
white duck; blue bonnet;
pink and blue shawl
Issued: Jan. 1993-Dec. 1993
Series: 100th Anniversary of Peter
Rabbit (1893-1993)

PRICING DATA	U.K. £	U.S. $	Can. $
Made in U.K.	30.00	45.00	65.00

JEREMY FISHER™

TECHNICAL DATA

Model No.: CBP04
Modeller: Richard Wawrzesta
Height: 3 ½", 8.9 cm
Colour: Cream and green box;
green frog; white jacket
Issued: Jan. 1993-Dec. 1993
Series: 100th Anniversary of Peter
Rabbit (1893-1993)

PRICING DATA	U.K. £	U.S. $	Can. $
Made in U.K.	30.00	45.00	65.00

MRS. TIGGY-WINKLE™

TECHNICAL DATA

Model No.: CBP05
Modeller: Richard Wawrzesta
Height: 3 ½", 8.9 cm
Colour: Cream and brown box;
Mrs. Tiggy-Winkle in
pink and white
Issued: Jan. 1993-Dec. 1993
Series: 100th Anniversary of Peter
Rabbit (1893-1993)

PRICING DATA	U.K. £	U.S. $	Can. $
Made in U.K.	30.00	45.00	65.00

TRINKET BOXES

PETER RABBIT™
First Variation

TECHNICAL DATA

Model No.:	CBP03
Modeller:	Richard Wawrzesta
Height:	3 ¾", 9.5 cm
Colour:	Brown rabbit; blue jacket; red and white handkerchief
Issued:	Jan. 1993-Dec. 1993
Series:	100th Anniversary of Peter Rabbit (1893-1993)

PRICING DATA	U.K. £	U.S. $	Can. $
Made in U.K.	60.00	95.00	125.00

PETER RABBIT™
Second Variation

TECHNICAL DATA

Model No.:	CBP17
Modeller:	Richard Wawrzesta
Height:	3 ½", 8.9 cm
Colour:	Brown and white rabbit; blue jacket; red and white handkerchief
Issued:	Jan. 1994-Dec. 1995

PRICING DATA	U.K. £	U.S. $	Can. $
Made in U.K.	30.00	45.00	65.00

WALL PLAQUES

AUNT PETTITOES AND PIGLETS™

TECHNICAL DATA

Model No.: 646806
Modeller: Richard Wawrzesta
Height: 5 ¼", 13.3 cm
Colour: Pink pig and piglets;
blue and white
striped shirt; green
skirt; grey pail
Issued: Jan. 2000 to the present

PRICING DATA	U.K. £	U.S. $	Can. $
Made Abroad	14.95	—	—

HUNCA MUNCA AND THE BABIES™

TECHNICAL DATA

Model No.: 646784
Modeller: Richard Wawrzesta
Height: 5 ¾", 14.6 cm
Colour: Brown mice; blue
dress with white
trim; copper kettle;
light brown basket;
pink blanket
Issued: June 1999 to the present

PRICING DATA	U.K. £	U.S. $	Can. $
Made Abroad	14.95	—	—

JEMIMA PUDDLE-DUCK™

TECHNICAL DATA

Model No.: 646814
Modeller: Richard Wawrzesta
Height: 5 ¼", 13.3 cm
Colour: Jemima: white duck;
rose-pink shawl; blue
bonnet
Foxy: green jacket and
pantaloons; red waistcoat
Issued: Jan. 2000 to the present

PRICING DATA	U.K. £	U.S. $	Can. $
Made Abroad	14.95	—	—

WALL PLAQUES

MR. JEREMY FISHER™

TECHNICAL DATA

Model No.:	648768
Modeller:	Richard Wawrzesta
Height:	4 ¾", 12.1 cm
Colour:	Yellowish-green frog; grey coat; green lilypad and reeds
Issued:	June 1999 to the present

PRICING DATA	U.K. £	U.S. $	Can. $
Made Abroad	14.95	—	—

MRS. RABBIT AND BABIES™

TECHNICAL DATA

Model No.:	646792
Modeller:	Richard Wawrzesta
Height:	5 ½", 14.0 cm
Colour:	Mrs. Rabbit: brown; blue dress; white apron Bunnies: brown; red cloaks Peter: brown; blue jacket
Issued:	Jan. 2000 to the present

PRICING DATA	U.K. £	U.S. $	Can. $
Made Abroad	14.95	—	—

MRS. TIGGY-WINKLE™

TECHNICAL DATA

Model No.:	648741
Modeller:	Richard Wawrzesta
Height:	5", 12.7 cm
Colour:	Brown hedgehog; white and rose shirt; blue and yellow striped skirt; tan basket; white linens
Issued:	June 1999 to the present

PRICING DATA	U.K. £	U.S. $	Can. $
Made Abroad	14.95	—	—

WALL PLAQUES

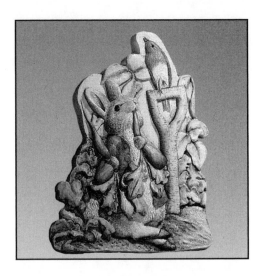

PETER RABBIT™

TECHNICAL DATA

Model No.: 648733
Modeller: Richard Wawrzesta
Height: 6 ¼", 15.9 cm
Colour: Brown rabbit;
blue jacket; red
radishes; tan spade
and bird
Issued: June 1999 to the present

PRICING DATA	U.K. £	U.S. $	Can. $
Made Abroad	14.95	—	—

THE TAILOR OF GLOUCESTER™

TECHNICAL DATA

Model No.: 646776
Modeller: Richard Wawrzesta
Height: 5 ½", 14.0 cm
Colour: Brown mouse;
white paper; tan
spool with fuchsia
thread; grey scissors
and thimble
Issued: Jan. 2000 to the present

PRICING DATA	U.K. £	U.S. $	Can. $
Made Abroad	14.95	—	—

WATERBALLS

JEMIMA PUDDLE-DUCK™

TECHNICAL DATA

Model No.:	590169
Modeller:	Richard Wawrzesta
Height:	4 ¾", 12.1 cm
Colour:	White duck; rose-pink and blue shawl; blue bonnet; yellow ducklings; green base with pink flowers
Issued:	June 1999 to the present

PRICING DATA	U.K. £	U.S. $	Can. $
Made Abroad	24.95	—	—

MRS. TIGGY-WINKLE™

TECHNICAL DATA

Model No.:	590134
Modeller:	Richard Wawrzesta
Height:	4 ¾", 12.1 cm
Colour:	Brown hedgehog: pink dress: white apron and cap; tan basket; green, grey, brown and pink base
Issued:	June 1999 to the present

PRICING DATA	U.K. £	U.S. $	Can. $
Made Abroad	24.95	—	—

WATERBALLS

PETER RABBIT™

TECHNICAL DATA

Model No.:	590142
Modeller:	Richard Wawrzesta
Height:	4 ¾", 12.1 cm
Colour:	Brown rabbit; blue jacket; orange and green radishes; brown spade and bird; grey, green, orange and tan base
Issued:	June 1999 to the present

PRICING DATA	U.K. £	U.S. $	Can. $
Made Abroad	24.95	—	—

THE TAILOR OF GLOUCESTER™

TECHNICAL DATA

Model No.:	590126
Modeller:	Richard Wawrzesta
Height:	4 ¾", 12.1 cm
Colour:	Brown mouse; white paper; tan spool with fuchsia thread; brown, grey, blue and white base
Issued:	June 1999 to the present

PRICING DATA	U.K. £	U.S. $	Can. $
Made Abroad	24.95	—	—

BRAMBLY HEDGE

Figurines
Cameos
Clocks
Musicals
Tableaux
Miscellaneous

FIGURINES
THE MIDWINTER COLLECTION

BASIL RECLINING™

TECHNICAL DATA

Model No.:	BH38
Designer:	Jill Barklem
Modeller:	Richard Wawrzesta
Height:	2 ¼", 5.7 cm
Colour:	Brown, white and pink mouse; red waistcoat; white and blue trousers; brown jacket
Issued:	July 1991-Dec. 1995
Packaging:	Tin

PRICING DATA	U.K. £	U.S. $	Can. $
Made in U.K.	125.00	200.00	275.00

LADY WOODMOUSE IN A CHAIR™

TECHNICAL DATA

Model No.:	BH21
Designer:	Jill Barklem
Modeller:	Richard Wawrzesta
Height:	3", 7.6 cm
Colour:	Brown, white and pink mouse; buff clothing
Issued:	July 1990-Dec. 1993
Packaging:	Tin

PRICING DATA	U.K. £	U.S. $	Can. $
Made in U.K.	200.00	300.00	400.00

LORD WOODMOUSE IN A CHAIR™

TECHNICAL DATA

Model No.:	BH22
Designer:	Jill Barklem
Modeller:	Richard Wawrzesta
Height:	3", 7.6 cm
Colour:	Brown, white and pink mouse; orange, blue and yellow clothing
Issued:	July 1990-Dec. 1993
Packaging:	Tin

PRICING DATA	U.K. £	U.S. $	Can. $
Made in U.K.	175.00	275.00	375.00

FIGURINES
THE MIDWINTER COLLECTION

MIDWINTER FIREPLACE™

TECHNICAL DATA

Model No.:	BH24
Designer:	Jill Barklem
Modeller:	Richard Wawrzesta
Height:	4 ¾", 12.1 cm
Colour:	Yellow and brown with multicoloured ornaments
Issued:	July 1990-Dec. 1993
Packaging:	Box

PRICING DATA	U.K. £	U.S. $	Can. $
Made in U.K.	150.00	225.00	300.00

MIDWINTER TREE™

TECHNICAL DATA

Model No.:	BH23
Designer:	Jill Barklem
Modeller:	Richard Wawrzesta
Height:	5 ½", 14.0 cm
Colour:	Green tree; yellow, orange and pink decorations
Issued:	July 1990-Dec. 1993
Packaging:	Box

PRICING DATA	U.K. £	U.S. $	Can. $
Made in U.K.	175.00	275.00	375.00

MRS. APPLE AND THE CHILDREN™

TECHNICAL DATA

Model No.:	BH37
Designer:	Jill Barklem
Modeller:	Richard Wawrzesta
Height:	2 ½", 6.4 cm
Colour:	Brown, white and pink mice; blue and white, red and white and yellow and white clothing
Issued:	July 1991-Dec. 1995
Packaging:	Tin

PRICING DATA	U.K. £	U.S. $	Can. $
Made in U.K.	150.00	225.00	300.00

FIGURINES
THE MIDWINTER COLLECTION

PRIMROSE RECITING™

TECHNICAL DATA

Model No.:	BH20
Designer:	Jill Barklem
Modeller:	Richard Wawrzesta
Height:	2 ½", 6.4 cm
Colour:	Brown, white and pink mouse; cream, blue and yellow hat
Issued:	July 1990-Dec. 1993
Packaging:	Tin

PRICING DATA	U.K. £	U.S. $	Can. $
Made in U.K.	150.00	225.00	300.00

SNOWMOUSE™

TECHNICAL DATA

Model No.:	BH18
Designer:	Jill Barklem
Modeller:	Richard Wawrzesta
Height:	2 ½", 6.4 cm
Colour:	White mouse; orange and white scarf; brown pipe
Issued:	July 1990-Dec. 1993
Packaging:	Tin

PRICING DATA	U.K. £	U.S. $	Can. $
Made in U.K.	50.00	75.00	110.00

WILFRED RECITING™

TECHNICAL DATA

Model No.:	BH19
Designer:	Jill Barklem
Modeller:	Richard Wawrzesta
Height:	2 ½", 6.4 cm
Colour:	Brown and pink mouse; blue and yellow hat; red clothing
Issued:	July 1990-Dec. 1993
Packaging:	Tin

PRICING DATA	U.K. £	U.S. $	Can. $
Made in U.K.	150.00	225.00	300.00

FIGURINES
THE MIDWINTER COLLECTION

THE MIDWINTER POINT OF SALE DISPLAY

TECHNICAL DATA

Model No.:	DISP3
Designer:	Jill Barklem
Modeller:	Richard Wawrzesta
Height:	6 ¾", 17.2 cm
Colour:	Cream and peach
Issued:	Jan.1991-by 1992

PRICING DATA	U.K. £	U.S. $	Can. $
Made in U.K.	30.00	60.00	75.00

Note: Display does not include figurines.

FIGURINES
THE NURSERY COLLECTION

THE BUNK BEDS™

TECHNICAL DATA

Model No.:	BH35
Designer:	Jill Barklem
Modeller:	Richard Wawrzesta
Height:	4 ¼", 10.8 cm
Colour:	Brown frame; pink and white and blue and white bedclothes
Issued:	Jan. 1991-Dec. 1995
Packaging:	Box

PRICING DATA	U.K. £	U.S. $	Can. $
Made in U.K.	130.00	200.00	275.00

THE CANOPY BED™

TECHNICAL DATA

Model No.:	BH34
Designer:	Jill Barklem
Modeller:	Richard Wawrzesta
Height:	6", 15.0 cm
Colour:	Multicoloured
Issued:	Jan. 1991-Dec. 1995
Packaging:	Box

PRICING DATA	U.K. £	U.S. $	Can. $
Made in U.K.	175.00	275.00	375.00

CLOVER AND CATKIN™

TECHNICAL DATA

Model No.:	BH32
Designer:	Jill Barklem
Modeller:	Richard Wawrzesta
Height:	2 ½", 6.4 cm
Colour:	Brown mice in white and pink bedclothes
Issued:	Jan. 1991-Dec. 1995
Packaging:	Tin

PRICING DATA	U.K. £	U.S. $	Can. $
Made in U.K.	65.00	100.00	150.00

FIGURINES
THE NURSERY COLLECTION

THE DRESSING TABLE™

TECHNICAL DATA

Model No.:	BH33
Designer:	Jill Barklem
Modeller:	Richard Wawrzesta
Height:	2 ¾", 7.0 cm
Colour:	Brown table; multi-coloured accessories
Issued:	Jan. 1991-Dec. 1995
Packaging:	Box

PRICING DATA	U.K. £	U.S. $	Can. $
Made in U.K.	130.00	200.00	275.00

LADY WOODMOUSE AND PRIMROSE™

TECHNICAL DATA

Model No.:	BH29
Designer:	Jill Barklem
Modeller:	Richard Wawrzesta
Height:	2 ¾", 7.0 cm
Colour:	Lady Woodmouse: pink, white and blue Primrose: yellow and white
Issued:	Jan. 1991-Dec. 1994
Packaging:	Tin

PRICING DATA	U.K. £	U.S. $	Can. $
Made in U.K.	150.00	225.00	300.00

PRIMROSE - TEDDY MOUSE™

TECHNICAL DATA

Model No.:	BH40
Designer:	Jill Barklem
Modeller:	Richard Wawrzesta
Height:	2 ¼", 5.7 cm
Colour:	Brown mouse in white and blue pyjamas
Issued:	Jan. 1992-Dec. 1996
Packaging:	Tin or box

PRICING DATA	U.K. £	U.S. $	Can. $
Made in U.K.	45.00	75.00	100.00

FIGURINES
THE NURSERY COLLECTION

TEASEL™

TECHNICAL DATA

Model No.:	BH30
Designer:	Jill Barklem
Modeller:	Richard Wawrzesta
Height:	2 ½", 6.4 cm
Colour:	Pink and white pyjamas; baby in blue
Issued:	Jan. 1991-Dec. 1996
Packaging:	Tin or box

PRICING DATA	U.K. £	U.S. $	Can. $
Made in U.K.	30.00	60.00	75.00

THE TOY CHEST™

TECHNICAL DATA

Model No.:	BH36
Designer:	Jill Barklem
Modeller:	Richard Wawrzesta
Height:	2 ½", 6.4 cm
Colour:	Green chest with tan trim; multi-coloured contents
Issued:	Jan. 1991-Dec. 1995
Packaging:	Tin

PRICING DATA	U.K. £	U.S. $	Can. $
Made in U.K.	40.00	65.00	90.00

WILFRED - TEDDY MOUSE™

TECHNICAL DATA

Model No.:	BH39
Designer:	Jill Barklem
Modeller:	Richard Wawrzesta
Height:	2 ½", 6.4 cm
Colour:	Red and white striped pyjamas; baby in blue
Issued:	Jan. 1992-Dec. 1996
Packaging:	Tin or box

PRICING DATA	U.K. £	U.S. $	Can. $
Made in U.K.	45.00	75.00	100.00

FIGURINES
THE NURSERY COLLECTION

WILFRED JIGGING™

TECHNICAL DATA

Model No.:	BH31
Designer:	Jill Barklem
Modeller:	Richard Wawrzesta
Height:	2 ½", 6.4 cm
Colour:	Brown mouse; red and white striped shirt
Issued:	Jan. 1991-Dec. 1996
Packaging:	Tin or box

PRICING DATA	U.K. £	U.S. $	Can. $
Made in U.K.	40.00	65.00	90.00

THE NURSERY POINT OF SALE DISPLAY

TECHNICAL DATA

Model No.:	DISP4
Designer:	Jill Barklem
Modeller:	Richard Wawrzesta
Height:	6 ¾", 17.2 cm
Colour:	Beige and white
Issued:	Jan. 1991-by 1992

PRICING DATA	U.K. £	U.S. $	Can. $
Made in U.K.	30.00	60.00	75.00

Note: Display does not include figurines.

FIGURINES
THE PICNIC COLLECTION

BASIL WITH BASKET™

TECHNICAL DATA

Model No.:	BH64
Designer:	Jill Barklem
Modeller:	Richard Wawrzesta
Height:	2 ½", 6.4 cm
Colour:	Green jacket; red waistcoat; blue and white striped trousers; brown baskets
Issued:	Jan. 1993-Dec. 1995
Packaging:	Tin

PRICING DATA	U.K. £	U.S. $	Can. $
Made in U.K.	70.00	110.00	150.00

LORD AND LADY WOODMOUSE RESTING™

TECHNICAL DATA

Model No.:	BH67
Designer:	Jill Barklem
Modeller:	Richard Wawrzesta
Height:	2 ¼", 5.7 cm
Colour:	Pink and white striped dress; white apron; blue trousers; red waistcoat
Issued:	Jan. 1993-Dec. 1995
Packaging:	Tin

PRICING DATA	U.K. £	U.S. $	Can. $
Made in U.K.	175.00	275.00	375.00

MR. TOADFLAX™

TECHNICAL DATA

Model No.:	BH61
Designer:	Jill Barklem
Modeller:	Richard Wawrzesta
Height:	2 ¾", 7.0 cm
Colour:	Blue waistcoat; pink and white striped shirt; brown basket
Issued:	Jan. 1993-Dec. 1995
Packaging:	Tin

PRICING DATA	U.K. £	U.S. $	Can. $
Made in U.K.	40.00	65.00	90.00

FIGURINES
THE PICNIC COLLECTION

MRS. APPLE AND WILFRED™

TECHNICAL DATA

Model No.:	BH65
Designer:	Jill Barklem
Modeller:	Richard Wawrzesta
Height:	2 ¾", 7.0 cm
Colour:	Blue and white striped dress; white apron; red and white striped shirt; blue trousers; brown wheelbarrow
Issued:	Jan. 1993-Dec. 1995
Packaging:	Tin

PRICING DATA	U.K. £	U.S. $	Can. $
Made in U.K.	250.00	400.00	550.00

MRS. TOADFLAX WITH HAMPER™

TECHNICAL DATA

Model No.:	BH62
Designer:	Jill Barklem
Modeller:	Richard Wawrzesta
Height:	2 ½", 6.4 cm
Colour:	White dress with yellow flowers; white apron; brown picnic hamper
Issued:	Jan. 1993-Dec. 1995
Packaging:	Tin

PRICING DATA	U.K. £	U.S. $	Can. $
Made in U.K.	125.00	200.00	275.00

PICNIC BLANKET™

TECHNICAL DATA

Model No.:	BH60
Designer:	Jill Barklem
Modeller:	Richard Wawrzesta
Height:	1 ½", 3.8 cm
Colour:	Multicoloured food on white blanket; green grass
Issued:	Jan. 1993-Dec. 1995
Packaging:	Box

PRICING DATA	U.K. £	U.S. $	Can. $
Made in U.K.	50.00	75.00	110.00

FIGURINES
THE PICNIC COLLECTION

TEASEL AND CLOVER™

TECHNICAL DATA

Model No.:	BH66
Designer:	Jill Barklem
Modeller:	Richard Wawrzesta
Height:	2 ½", 6.4 cm
Colour:	Rose-pink dress; white apron; blue dungarees; white and blue striped shirt
Issued:	Jan. 1993-Dec. 1995
Packaging:	Tin

PRICING DATA	U.K. £	U.S. $	Can. $
Made in U.K.	90.00	150.00	200.00

Note: A few figurines exist with Teasel wearing a red striped shirt. These models are very rare.

WILFRED WITH TOYS™

TECHNICAL DATA

Model No.:	BH63
Designer:	Jill Barklem
Modeller:	Richard Wawrzesta
Height:	2", 5.0 cm
Colour:	Blue dungarees; white and red striped shirt; multicoloured toys
Issued:	Jan. 1993-Dec. 1995
Packaging:	Tin

PRICING DATA	U.K. £	U.S. $	Can. $
Made in U.K.	150.00	225.00	300.00

FIGURINES
POPPY'S BABIES COLLECTION

BABIES IN THE BATH™

TECHNICAL DATA

Model No.:	BH73
Designer:	Jill Barklem
Modeller:	Richard Wawrzesta
Height:	2 ¼", 5.7 cm
Colour:	Brown, white and pink mice in blue tub; yellow sponge
Issued:	Jan. 1996-Dec. 1997
Packaging:	Box

PRICING DATA	U.K. £	U.S. $	Can. $
Made in U.K.	65.00	100.00	150.00

DUSTY PUSHING PRAM™

TECHNICAL DATA

Model No.:	BH75
Designer:	Jill Barklem
Modeller:	Richard Wawrzesta
Height:	3", 7.6 cm
Colour:	Brown and white mouse; grey, blue and white clothing; brown pram; pink and white blanket
Issued:	Jan. 1996-Dec. 1997
Packaging:	Box

PRICING DATA	U.K. £	U.S. $	Can. $
Made in U.K.	65.00	100.00	150.00

LADY WOODMOUSE LOOKING IN THE CRADLE™

TECHNICAL DATA

Model No.:	BH71
Designer:	Jill Barklem
Modeller:	Richard Wawrzesta
Height:	3", 7.6 cm
Colour:	White, red, blue and yellow clothing; brown cradle; multicoloured blanket
Issued:	Jan. 1996-Dec. 1997
Packaging:	Box

PRICING DATA	U.K. £	U.S. $	Can. $
Made in U.K.	65.00	100.00	150.00

FIGURINES
POPPY'S BABIES COLLECTION

POPPY AND BABIES™

TECHNICAL DATA

Model No.:	BH70
Designer:	Jill Barklem
Modeller:	Richard Wawrzesta
Height:	3", 7.6 cm
Colour:	Brown, white and pink mice; blue, white and red clothing
Issued:	Jan. 1996-Dec. 1997
Packaging:	Box

PRICING DATA	U.K. £	U.S. $	Can. $
Made in U.K.	65.00	100.00	150.00

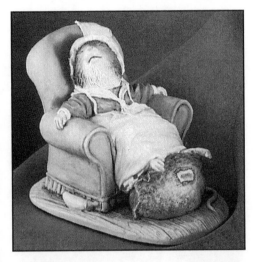

POPPY ASLEEP IN CHAIR™

TECHNICAL DATA

Model No.:	BH72
Designer:	Jill Barklem
Modeller:	Richard Wawrzesta
Height:	2 ¼", 5.7 cm
Colour:	Brown and white mouse; blue and white clothing; green chair; brown cushion
Issued:	Jan. 1996-Dec. 1997
Packaging:	Box

PRICING DATA	U.K. £	U.S. $	Can. $
Made in U.K.	65.00	100.00	150.00

POPPY PACKING NIGHT CLOTHES™

TECHNICAL DATA

Model No.:	BH74
Designer:	Jill Barklem
Modeller:	Richard Wawrzesta
Height:	2 ½", 6.4 cm
Colour:	Brown and white mouse; blue, white and red clothing; brown trunk
Issued:	Jan. 1996-Dec. 1997
Packaging:	Box

PRICING DATA	U.K. £	U.S. $	Can. $
Made in U.K.	65.00	100.00	150.00

FIGURINES
THE STORE STUMP KITCHEN COLLECTION

BASIL WITH BOTTLES™

TECHNICAL DATA

Model No.:	BH26
Designer:	Jill Barklem
Modeller:	Richard Wawrzesta
Height:	2 ½", 6.4 cm
Colour:	Brown, white and pink mouse; red waistcoat; blue and white striped trousers
Issued:	Jan. 1991-Dec. 1996
Packaging:	Tin or box

PRICING DATA	U.K. £	U.S. $	Can. $
Made in U.K.	30.00	60.00	75.00

THE DRESSER™

PRICING DATA

Model No.:	BH6
Designer:	Jill Barklem
Modeller:	Richard Wawrzesta
Height:	5", 12.7 cm
Colour:	Cream dresser with multicoloured contents
Issued:	Jan. 1988-Dec. 1995
Packaging:	Box

PRICING DATA	U.K. £	U.S. $	Can. $
Made in U.K.	125.00	200.00	275.00

THE FIREPLACE™

TECHNICAL DATA

Model No.:	BH8
Designer:	Jill Barklem
Modeller:	Richard Wawrzesta
Height:	5", 12.7 cm
Colour:	Cream hearth with multicoloured contents
Issued:	Jan. 1988-Dec. 1995
Packaging:	Box

PRICING DATA	U.K. £	U.S. $	Can. $
Made in U.K.	135.00	215.00	300.00

FIGURINES
THE STORE STUMP KITCHEN COLLECTION

LADY WOODMOUSE™

TECHNICAL DATA

Model No.:	BH2
Designer:	Jill Barklem
Modeller:	Richard Wawrzesta
Height:	2 ½", 6.4 cm
Colour:	Pink dress; white apron; straw hat and basket
Issued:	Jan. 1988-Dec. 1996
Packaging:	Tin or box

PRICING DATA	U.K. £	U.S. $	Can. $
Made in U.K.	30.00	60.00	75.00

MR. APPLE IN ROCKING CHAIR™

TECHNICAL DATA

Model No.:	BH5
Designer:	Jill Barklem
Modeller:	Richard Wawrzesta
Height:	3 ¼", 8.3 cm
Colour:	Blue trousers and waistcoat; pale blue shirt; white tablecloth; red checkered cloth
Issued:	Jan. 1988-Dec. 1995
Packaging:	Tin

PRICING DATA	U.K. £	U.S. $	Can. $
Made in U.K.	80.00	125.00	175.00

MRS. APPLE™

TECHNICAL DATA

Model No.:	BH1
Designer:	Jill Barklem
Modeller:	Richard Wawrzesta
Height:	2 ½", 6.4 cm
Colour:	Blue striped dress; white apron; green tea service
Issued:	Jan. 1988-Dec. 1996
Packaging:	Tin or box

PRICING DATA	U.K. £	U.S. $	Can. $
Made in U.K.	30.00	60.00	75.00

FIGURINES
THE STORE STUMP KITCHEN COLLECTION

MRS. CRUSTY BREAD WITH MIXING BOWL™

TECHNICAL DATA

Model No.:	BH25
Designer:	Jill Barklem
Modeller:	Richard Wawrzesta
Height:	2 ½", 6.4 cm
Colour:	Brown and white mouse; white apron; yellow dress; white bowl
Issued:	Jan. 1991-Dec. 1996
Packaging:	Tin or box

PRICING DATA	U.K. £	U.S. $	Can. $
Made in U.K.	30.00	60.00	75.00

PRIMROSE™

TECHNICAL DATA

Model No.:	BH3
Designer:	Jill Barklem
Modeller:	Richard Wawrzesta
Height:	2 ¼", 5.7 cm
Colour:	Yellow dress; white apron and cloth
Issued:	Jan. 1988-Dec. 1996
Packaging:	Tin or box

PRICING DATA	U.K. £	U.S. $	Can. $
Made in U.K.	30.00	60.00	75.00

THE TABLE™

TECHNICAL DATA

Model No.:	BH7
Designer:	Jill Barklem
Modeller:	Richard Wawrzesta
Height:	3", 7.6 cm
Colour:	Cream table with multicoloured contents
Issued:	Jan. 1988-Dec. 1995
Packaging:	Box

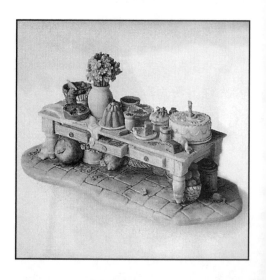

PRICING DATA	U.K. £	U.S. $	Can. $
Made in U.K.	125.00	200.00	275.00

FIGURINES
THE STORE STUMP KITCHEN COLLECTION

WILFRED™

TECHNICAL DATA

Model No.:	BH4
Designer:	Jill Barklem
Modeller:	Richard Wawrzesta
Height:	2 ¼", 5.7 cm
Colour:	Blue dungarees; red and white striped shirt
Issued:	Jan. 1988-Dec. 1996
Packaging:	Tin or box

PRICING DATA	U.K. £	U.S. $	Can. $
Made in U.K.	30.00	60.00	75.00

THE KITCHEN POINT OF SALE DISPLAY

TECHNICAL DATA

Model No.:	DISP1
Designer:	Jill Barklem
Modeller:	Richard Wawrzesta
Height:	6 ¾", 17.2 cm
Colour:	Cream and brown
Issued:	Unknown-by 1992

PRICING DATA	U.K. £	U.S. $	Can. $
Made in U.K.	30.00	60.00	75.00

Note: Display does not include figurines.

FIGURINES
THE WEDDING COLLECTION

BEST MAN - CONKER™

TECHNICAL DATA

Model No.:	BH15
Designer:	Jill Barklem
Modeller:	Richard Wawrzesta
Height:	2 ½", 6.4 cm
Colour:	Green waistcoat; green and white striped trousers; blue and pink present
Issued:	Jan. 1990-Dec. 1996
Packaging:	Tin or box

PRICING DATA	U.K. £	U.S. $	Can. $
Made in U.K.	35.00	50.00	80.00

BRIDE - POPPY EYEBRIGHT™

TECHNICAL DATA

Model No.:	BH9
Designer:	Jill Barklem
Modeller:	Richard Wawrzesta
Height:	2 ½", 6.4 cm
Colour:	Pink and white striped dress; white and blue apron
Issued:	Jan. 1989-Dec. 1996
Packaging:	Tin or box

PRICING DATA	U.K. £	U.S. $	Can. $
Made in U.K.	30.00	60.00	75.00

BRIDE AND GROOM - POPPY AND DUSTY™

TECHNICAL DATA

Model No.:	BH11
Designer:	Jill Barklem
Modeller:	Richard Wawrzesta
Height:	2 ½", 6.4 cm
Colour:	Pink and white striped dress; white and blue apron; violet suit; rose waistcoat
Issued:	Jan. 1990-Dec. 1995
Packaging:	Tin or box

PRICING DATA	U.K. £	U.S. $	Can. $
Made in U.K.	50.00	75.00	110.00

FIGURINES
THE WEDDING COLLECTION

BRIDESMAID - PRIMROSE™

TECHNICAL DATA

Model No.: BH14
Designer: Jill Barklem
Modeller: Richard Wawrzesta
Height: 2 ¼", 5.7 cm
Colour: Pink dress; white apron; multicoloured flowers
Issued: Jan. 1990-Dec. 1996
Packaging: Tin or box

PRICING DATA	U.K. £	U.S. $	Can. $
Made in U.K.	30.00	60.00	75.00

FLORAL ARCH™

TECHNICAL DATA

Model No.: BH16
Designer: Jill Barklem
Modeller: Richard Wawrzesta
Height: 5 ½", 14.0 cm
Colour: Green, pink, yellow and blue
Issued: Jan. 1990-Dec. 1995
Packaging: Box

PRICING DATA	U.K. £	U.S. $	Can. $
Made in U.K.	125.00	200.00	275.00

GROOM - DUSTY DOGWOOD™

TECHNICAL DATA

Model No.: BH10
Designer: Jill Barklem
Modeller: Richard Wawrzesta
Height: 2 ½", 6.4 cm
Colour: Blue suit; rose waistcoat; white shirt
Issued: Jan. 1989-Dec. 1996
Packaging: Tin or box

PRICING DATA	U.K. £	U.S. $	Can. $
Made in U.K.	30.00	60.00	75.00

FIGURINES
THE WEDDING COLLECTION
LADY WOODMOUSE EATING CAKE™

TECHNICAL DATA

Model No.:	BH28
Designer:	Jill Barklem
Modeller:	Richard Wawrzesta
Height:	2 ¾", 7.0 cm
Colour:	Tan bonnet; blue frock; white apron
Issued:	Jan. 1991-Dec. 1996
Packaging:	Tin or box

PRICING DATA	U.K. £	U.S. $	Can. $
Made in U.K.	30.00	60.00	75.00

MINISTER - OLD VOLE™

TECHNICAL DATA

Model No.:	BH12
Modeller:	Richard Wawrzesta
Height:	2 ¼", 5.7 cm
Colour:	Brown; green jacket and waistcoat; blue trousers
Issued:	Jan. 1990-Dec. 1996
Packaging:	Tin or box

PRICING DATA	U.K. £	U.S. $	Can. $
Made in U.K.	50.00	75.00	110.00

MR. APPLE PROPOSING A TOAST™

TECHNICAL DATA

Model No.:	BH27
Designer:	Jill Barklem
Modeller:	Richard Wawrzesta
Height:	2 ¾", 7.0 cm
Colour:	Blue jacket and trousers; white shirt; red bowtie
Issued:	Jan. 1991-Dec. 1996
Packaging:	Tin or box

PRICING DATA	U.K. £	U.S. $	Can. $
Made in U.K.	30.00	60.00	75.00

FIGURINES
THE WEDDING COLLECTION

PAGEBOY - WILFRED™

TECHNICAL DATA

Model No.:	BH13
Designer:	Jill Barklem
Modeller:	Richard Wawrzesta
Height:	2 ¼", 5.7 cm
Colour:	Brown and white mouse; blue clothing
Issued:	Jan. 1990-Dec. 1996
Packaging:	Tin or box

PRICING DATA	U.K. £	U.S. $	Can. $
Made in U.K.	30.00	60.00	75.00

WEDDING TABLE AND CANOPY™

TECHNICAL DATA

Model No.:	BH17
Designer:	Jill Barklem
Modeller:	Richard Wawrzesta
Height:	5 ¼", 13.3 cm
Colour:	Pink and white awning; blue background; multicoloured food
Issued:	Jan. 1990-Dec. 1995
Packaging:	Box

PRICING DATA	U.K. £	U..S. $	Can. $
Made in U.K.	125.00	200.00	275.00

THE WEDDING POINT OF SALE DISPLAY

TECHNICAL DATA

Model No.:	DISP2
Designer:	Jill Barklem
Modeller:	Richard Wawrzesta
Height:	6 ¾", 17.2 cm
Colour:	Cream and green
Issued:	Unknown-by 1992

PRICING DATA	U.K. £	U.S. $	Can. $
Made in U.K.	30.00	60.00	75.00

Note: Display does not include figurines.

CAMEOS

HARVEST MICE CAMEO™

TECHNICAL DATA

Model No.:	BH105
Designer:	Jill Barklem
Modeller:	Richard Wawrzesta
Height:	4 ¼", 10.8 cm
Colour:	Brown and tan frame; brown and white mice in blue, white and yellow; multicoloured background
Issued:	June 1991-Dec. 1994

PRICING DATA	U.K. £	U.S. $	Can. $
Made in U.K.	150.00	250.00	325.00

SNOWY WINDOW CAMEO™

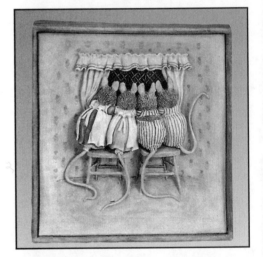

TECHNICAL DATA

Model No.:	BH107
Designer:	Jill Barklem
Modeller:	Richard Wawrzesta
Height:	4 ¼", 10.8 cm
Colour:	Grey-green frame; pink and green background; brown, white and pink mice in pink, white, yellow and blue
Issued:	June 1991-Dec. 1994

PRICING DATA	U.K. £	U.S. $	Can. $
Made in U.K.	150.00	250.00	325.00

SUPPER BY THE FIRE CAMEO™

TECHNICAL DATA

Model No.:	BH106
Designer:	Jill Barklem
Modeller:	Richard Wawrzesta
Height:	4 ½", 11.9 cm
Colour:	Brown frame; brown, white and pink mice; multicoloured background
Issued:	June 1991-Dec. 1994

PRICING DATA	U.K. £	U.S. $	Can. $
Made in U.K.	150.00	250.00	325.00

CLOCKS

NURSERY CLOCK™

TECHNICAL DATA

Model No.:	BH101
Designer:	Jill Barklem
Modeller:	Richard Wawrzesta
Height:	8 ¼", 21.0 cm
Colour:	Pink, white, blue and cream
Issued:	Jan. 1992-Dec. 1997

PRICING DATA	U.K. £	U.S. $	Can. $
Made in U.K.	75.00	110.00	150.00

POPPY'S BABIES CLOCK™

TECHNICAL DATA

Model No.:	BH102
Designer:	Jill Barklem
Modeller:	Richard Wawrzesta
Height:	6 ½", 16.5 cm
Colour:	Cream wall; brown cradles; blue and white windows
Issued:	Jan. 1996-Dec. 1997

PRICING DATA	U.K. £	U.S. $	Can. $
Made in U.K.	75.00	110.00	150.00

STORE STUMP CLOCK™

TECHNICAL DATA

Model No.:	BH100
Designer:	Jill Barklem
Modeller:	Richard Wawrzesta
Height:	8 ¼", 21.0 cm
Colour:	Brown shelves with multicoloured contents
Issued:	June 1991-Dec. 1997

PRICING DATA	U.K. £	U.S. $	Can. $
Made in U.K.	100.00	150.00	200.00

MUSICALS

MRS. APPLE™

TECHNICAL DATA

Model No.:	BH53
Designer:	Jill Barklem
Modeller:	Richard Wawrzesta
Height:	4", 10.1 cm
Colour:	Brown mouse; blue and white striped dress; white apron; green tea service
Issued:	Jan. 1990-Dec. 1995

PRICING DATA	U.K. £	U.S. $	Can. $
Made in U.K.	85.00	135.00	175.00

POPPY EYEBRIGHT™

TECHNICAL DATA

Model No.:	BH52
Designer:	Jill Barklem
Modeller:	Richard Wawrzesta
Height:	4", 10.1 cm
Colour:	Brown mouse; red and white striped dress; white apron with blue flowers
Issued:	Jan. 1990-Dec. 1995

PRICING DATA	U.K. £	U.S. $	Can. $
Made in U.K.	85.00	135.00	175.00

MUSICALS

PRIMROSE™

TECHNICAL DATA

Model No.:	BH51
Designer:	Jill Barklem
Modeller:	Richard Wawrzesta
Height:	3 ½", 8.9 cm
Colour:	Brown mouse; yellow dress; white apron; tan basket; pink fruit
Issued:	Jan. 1990-Dec. 1995

PRICING DATA	U.K. £	U.S. $	Can. $
Made in U.K.	85.00	135.00	175.00

WILFRED™

TECHNICAL DATA

Model No.:	BH50
Designer:	Jill Barklem
Modeller:	Richard Wawrzesta
Height:	3 ½", 8.9 cm
Colour:	Brown mouse; blue overalls; multicoloured toys
Issued:	Jan. 1990-Dec. 1995

PRICING DATA	U.K. £	U.S. $	Can. $
Made in U.K.	85.00	135.00	175.00

TABLEAUX

AUTUMN™

TECHNICAL DATA

Model No.:	B0631
Designer:	Jill Barklem
Modeller:	Richard Wawrzesta
Size:	6 ¼" x 8", 15.9 cm x 20.3 cm
Colour:	Brown mice; yellow, white, tan and rust clothing; burnt orange and pinkish-brown leaves; dark purple berries
Issued:	Nov. 2000 in a limited edition of 999
Series:	Four Seasons Tableau Collection

PRICING DATA	U.K. £	U.S. $	Can. $
Made in U.K.	119.00	—	—

Note: Exclusive to Wheelers of Loughborough. A special backstamp for the 21st Century was used.

THE MILLENNIUM SNOW BALL TABLEAU™

TECHNICAL DATA

Model No.:	B0555
Designer:	Jill Barklem
Modeller:	Richard Wawrzesta
Size:	6 ½" x 9", 16.5 cm x 22.9 cm
Colour:	Brown mice; green, red, blue, yellow, white and cream clothing; white arch with green holly and red berries
Issued:	Jan. 1999 in a limited edition of 999

PRICING DATA	U.K. £	U.S. $	Can. $
Made in U.K.	119.00	—	—

Note: Exclusive to Wheelers of Loughborough.

TABLEAUX

SPRING™

TECHNICAL DATA

Model No.:	B0630
Designer:	Jill Barklem
Modeller:	Richard Wawrzesta
Size:	6 ½" x 7 ¾", 16.5 cm x 19.7 cm
Colour:	Brown mice; blue, white, green, red and yellow clothing; blue and pink flowers with green leaves
Issued:	Apr. 2000 in a limited edition of 999
Series:	Four Season Tableau Collection

PRICING DATA	U.K. £	U.S. $	Can. $
Made in U.K.	119.00	—	—

Note: Exclusive to Wheelers of Loughborough. A special backstamp for the 21st century was used.

SUMMER™

TECHNICAL DATA

Model No.:	B0514
Designer:	Jill Barklem
Modeller:	Richard Wawrzesta
Size:	6 ½" x 7 ¼", 16.5 cm x 18.4 cm
Colour:	Brown mice and mole; green, red and yellow clothing; pink, blue, yellow, white and green floral arch
Issued:	1999 in a limited edition of 999
Series:	Four Seasons Tableau Collection

PRICING DATA	U.K. £	U.S. $	Can. $
Made in U.K.	119.00	—	—

Note: Exclusive to Wheelers of Loughborough. A special backstamp for the 20th century was used.

TABLEAUX

WINTER™

TECHNICAL DATA

Model No.: B0554
Designer: Jill Barklem
Modeller: Richard Wawrzesta
Size: 6 ½" x 7 ¼", 16.5 cm x 18.4 cm
Colour: Blue and white striped dress and shirt; blue pants; red armchair; orange-yellow fire; brown fireplace with holly and red bows
Issued: October 1999 in a limited edition of 999
Series: Four Seasons Tableau Collection

PRICING DATA	U.K. £	U.S. $	Can. $
Made in U.K.	119.00	—	—

Note: Exclusive to Wheelers of Loughborough. A special backstamp for the 20th century was used.

MISCELLANEOUS

BOOKENDS

POPPY AND BABIES™

TECHNICAL DATA

Model No.:	BHB01
Designer:	Jill Barklem
Modeller:	Richard Wawrzesta
Height:	5 ¼", 13.3 cm
Colour:	Multicoloured
Issued:	Jan. 1996-Dec. 1997

PRICING DATA	U.K. £	U.S. $	Can. $
Made in U.K.	165.00	275.00	375.00

Note: Prices refer to the pair of bookends.

MONEY BOXES

ROSE IN HER CRADLE™

TECHNICAL DATA

Model No.:	BHMB01
Designer:	Jill Barklem
Modeller:	Richard Wawrzesta
Height:	6 ¼", 15.9 cm
Colour:	Brown and white mouse; brown cradle with pink canopy and trim; multicoloured blanket
Issued:	Jan. 1996-Dec. 1997
Series:	Poppy's Babies Collection

PRICING DATA	U.K. £	U.S. $	Can. $
Made in U.K.	30.00	60.00	75.00

MISCELLANEOUS

TRINKET BOXES

THE MILLENNIUM SNOW BALL™

TECHNICAL DATA

Model No.:	B0556
Designer:	Jill Barklem
Modeller:	Richard Wawrzesta
Height:	5", 12.7 cm
Colour:	Brown mice; rose-pink dress; white apron; blue coat; white box with bottle of Elderflower wine inside
Issued:	Jan. 2000 in a limited edition of 999

PRICING DATA	U.K. £	U.S. $	Can. $
Made in U.K.	29.95	—	—

Note: Exclusive to Wheelers of Loughborough.

WATERBALLS

BABIES IN THE BATH™

TECHNICAL DATA

Model No.:	BHW01
Designer:	Jill Barklem
Modeller:	Richard Wawrzesta
Height:	5", 12.7 cm
Colour:	Brown and white mice; blue tub; yellow sponge and rubber duckie
Issued:	Jan. 1996-Dec. 1997
Series:	Poppy's Babies Collection

PRICING DATA	U.K. £	U.S. $	Can. $
Made in U.K.	50.00	75.00	110.00

FAIRIES

Fairies by Cicely Mary Barker
Fairies by Linda Pagett

FIGURINES
FLOWER FAIRIES

APPLE BLOSSOM FAIRY™
Style One

TECHNICAL DATA

Model No.:	CF6
Designer:	Cicely Mary Barker
Modeller:	David Geenty
Height:	6 ¾", 17.2 cm
Colour:	Green and pink clothing; pink flowers
Issued:	Jan. 1986-Dec. 1987

PRICING DATA	U.K. £	U.S. $	Can. $
Made in U.K.	125.00	200.00	250.00

BLACKTHORN FAIRY™

TECHNICAL DATA

Model No.:	CF5
Designer:	Cicely Mary Barker
Modeller:	David Geenty
Height:	9", 22.9 cm
Colour:	Dark blue shirt; white skirt with red dots; pink blossoms; brown stem and thorns
Issued:	Jan. 1986-Dec. 1987

PRICING DATA	U.K. £	U.S. $	Can. $
Made in U.K.	100.00	150.00	200.00

BUGLE FAIRY™

TECHNICAL DATA

Model No.:	CF10
Designer:	Cicely Mary Barker
Modeller:	David Geenty
Height:	7 ½", 19.1 cm
Colour:	Blue and lilac clothing; blue flowers; green stem and leaves
Issued:	Jan. 1988-Dec. 1989

PRICING DATA	U.K. £	U.S. $	Can. $
Made in U.K.	100.00	150.00	200.00

FIGURINES
FLOWER FAIRIES

CANDYTUFT FAIRY™
Style One

TECHNICAL DATA

Model No.:	CF2
Designer:	Cicely Mary Barker
Modeller:	David Geenty
Height:	5", 12.7 cm
Colour:	Pink clothing and wings
Issued:	Jan. 1986-Dec. 1987

PRICING DATA	U.K. £	U.S. $	Can. $
Made in U.K.	75.00	125.00	160.00

COLUMBINE FAIRY™

TECHNICAL DATA

Model No.:	CF11
Designer:	Cicely Mary Barker
Modeller:	David Geenty
Height:	6 ¾", 17.2 cm
Colour:	Orange, rose-pink and green clothing; rose-pink flowers
Issued:	Jan. 1988-Dec. 1989

PRICING DATA	U.K. £	U.S. $	Can. $
Made in U.K.	100.00	150.00	200.00

FUCHSIA FAIRY™

TECHNICAL DATA

Model No.:	CF12
Designer:	Cicely Mary Barker
Modeller:	David Geenty
Height:	6 ¾", 17.2 cm
Colour:	Rose-pink and purple clothing; lilac wings; rose-pink and purple flower
Issued:	Jan. 1988-Dec. 1989

PRICING DATA	U.K. £	U.S. $	Can. $
Made in U.K.	100.00	150.00	200.00

FIGURINES
FLOWER FAIRIES

HELIOTROPE FAIRY™

TECHNICAL DATA

Model No.:	CF4
Designer:	Cicely Mary Barker
Modeller:	David Geenty
Height:	6 ¾", 17.2 cm
Colour:	Pink dress; lilac flowers
Issued:	Jan. 1986-Dec. 1987

PRICING DATA	U.K. £	U.S. $	Can. $
Made in U.K.	100.00	150.00	200.00

IRIS FAIRY™

TECHNICAL DATA

Model No.:	CF9
Designer:	Cicely Mary Barker
Modeller:	David Geenty
Height:	7 ½", 19.1 cm
Colour:	Yellow dress and flowers
Issued:	Jan. 1988-Dec. 1989

PRICING DATA	U.K. £	U.S. $	Can. $
Made in U.K.	100.00	150.00	200.00

LAVENDER FAIRY™
Style One

TECHNICAL DATA

Model No.:	CF1
Designer:	Cicely Mary Barker
Modeller:	David Geenty
Height:	8 ¾", 22.2 cm
Colour:	Lilac and green dress; lilac wings
Issued:	Jan. 1986-Dec. 1987

PRICING DATA	U.K. £	U.S. $	Can. $
Made in U.K.	100.00	150.00	200.00

FIGURINES
FLOWER FAIRIES

MALLOW FAIRY™

TECHNICAL DATA

Model No.:	CF8
Designer:	Cicely Mary Barker
Modeller:	David Geenty
Height:	7", 17.8 cm
Colour:	Green and lilac clothing; lilac flowers; green leaves
Issued:	Jan. 1988-Dec. 1989

PRICING DATA	U.K. £	U.S. $	Can. $
Made in U.K.	100.00	150.00	200.00

NASTURTIUM FAIRY™

TECHNICAL DATA

Model No.:	CF7
Designer:	Cicely Mary Barker
Modeller:	David Geenty
Height:	6", 15.0 cm
Colour:	Orange, yellow and green clothing
Issued:	Jan. 1988-Dec. 1989

PRICING DATA	U.K. £	U.S. $	Can. $
Made in U.K.	100.00	150.00	200.00

SWEET PEA FAIRY™
Style One

TECHNICAL DATA

Model No.:	CF3
Designer:	Cicely Mary Barker
Modeller:	David Geenty
Height:	7 ¼", 18.4 cm
Colour:	Green, rose-pink and lilac clothing
Issued:	Jan. 1986-Dec. 1987

PRICING DATA	U.K. £	U.S. $	Can. $
Made in U.K.	100.00	150.00	200.00

FIGURINES
FLOWER FAIRIES LIMITED EDITIONS

THE BLACKBERRY FAIRY™

TECHNICAL DATA

Model No.:	CF23
Designer:	Cicely Mary Barker
Modeller:	Glenis Devereux
Height:	5 ¾", 14.6 cm
Colour:	Blackberry dress; lilac wings; orange-brown leaves; purple berries
Issued:	Jan. 1993 in a limited edition of 1,950

PRICING DATA	U.K. £	U.S. $	Can. $
Made in U.K.	200.00	300.00	400.00

THE BUTTERCUP FAIRY™

TECHNICAL DATA

Model No.:	B0114
Designer:	Cicely Mary Barker
Modeller:	Glenis Devereux
Height:	7 ½", 19.1 cm
Colour:	Yellow dress and buttercups; green wings, stem and leaves
Issued:	Jan. 1997 in a limited edition of 1,950

PRICING DATA	U.K. £	U.S. $	Can. $
Made in U.K.	125.00	200.00	275.00

THE CHICORY FAIRY™

TECHNICAL DATA

Model No.:	CF22
Designer:	Cicely Mary Barker
Modeller:	Glenis Devereux
Height:	6 ¼", 15.9 cm
Colour:	Lilac dress, cap and flowers; cream and lilac wings; green leaves
Issued:	Jan. 1993 in a limited edition of 1,950

PRICING DATA	U.K. £	U.S. $	Can. $
Made in U.K.	150.00	250.00	325.00

FIGURINES
FLOWER FAIRIES LIMITED EDITIONS

THE GORSE FAIRY™

TECHNICAL DATA

Model No.:	CF21
Designer:	Cicely Mary Barker
Modeller:	Glenis Devereux
Height:	8", 20.3 cm
Colour:	Yellow, brown and green clothing; green-brown wings; yellow gorse
Issued:	Jan. 1993 in a limited edition of 1,950

PRICING DATA	U.K. £	U.S. $	Can. $
Made in U.K.	200.00	300.00	400.00

THE HOLLY FAIRY (WINTER)™

TECHNICAL DATA

Model No.:	B0417
Designer:	Cicely Mary Barker
Modeller:	Glenis Devereux
Height:	8 ¼", 21.0 cm
Colour:	Green, red and orange clothing
Issued:	Jan. 1999 in a limited edition of 1,950
Series:	Flower Fairies of the Seasons

PRICING DATA	U.K. £	U.S. $	Can. $
Made in U.K.	170.00	—	—

THE JASMINE FAIRY (SUMMER)™

TECHNICAL DATA

Model No.:	B0415
Designer:	Cicely Mary Barker
Modeller:	Glenis Devereux
Height:	6 ½", 16.5 cm
Colour:	Peach clothing; green leaves; white flowers with pink
Issued:	Jan. 1999 in a limited edition of 1,950
Series:	Flower Fairies of the Seasons

PRICING DATA	U.K. £	U.S. $	Can. $
Made in U.K.	125.00	—	—

FIGURINES
FLOWER FAIRIES LIMITED EDITIONS

THE MARIGOLD FAIRY™

TECHNICAL DATA

Model No.:	CF28
Designer:	Cicely Mary Barker
Modeller:	Glenis Devereux
Height:	6", 15.0 cm
Colour:	Green dress, wings and leaves
Issued:	Jan. 1996 in a limited edition of 1,950

PRICING DATA	U.K. £	U.S. $	Can. $
Made in U.K.	200.00	300.00	400.00

THE MILLENNIUM CHRISTMAS FAIRY™

TECHNICAL DATA

Model No.:	B0536
Designer:	Cicely Mary Barker
Modeller:	Glenis Devereux
Height:	7 ½", 19.1 cm
Colour:	White dress; peach wings
Issued:	Jan. 2000 in a limited edition of 500

PRICING DATA	U.K. £	U.S. $	Can. $
Made in U.K.	150.00	—	—

THE NARCISSUS FAIRY™

TECHNICAL DATA

Model No.:	CF24
Designer:	Cicely Mary Barker
Modeller:	Glenis Devereux
Height:	8 ¼", 21.0 cm
Colour:	White, yellow and red dress
Issued:	Jan. 1994 in a limited edition of 950

PRICING DATA	U.K. £	U.S. $	Can. $
Made in U.K.	200.00	300.00	400.00

FIGURINES
FLOWER FAIRIES LIMITED EDITIONS

THE PANSY FAIRY™

TECHNICAL DATA

Model No.:	CF29
Designer:	Cicely Mary Barker
Modeller:	Glenis Devereux
Height:	7 ¼", 18.4 cm
Colour:	Lilac and yellow dress; violet wings
Issued:	Jan. 1996 in a limited edition of 1,950

PRICING DATA	U.K. £	U.S. $	Can. $
Made in U.K.	200.00	300.00	400.00

THE PRIMROSE FAIRY (SPRING)™

TECHNICAL DATA

Model No.:	B0416
Designer:	Cicely Mary Barker
Modeller:	Glenis Devereux
Height:	7 ½", 19.1 cm
Colour:	Yellow and green clothing and flowers
Issued:	Jan. 1999 in a limited edition of 1,950
Series:	Flower Fairies of the Seasons

PRICING DATA	U.K. £	U.S. $	Can. $
Made in U.K.	125.00	—	—

THE ROSE FAIRY™
Style One

TECHNICAL DATA

Model No.:	CF20
Designer:	Cicely Mary Barker
Modeller:	Glenis Devereux
Height:	7 ½", 19.1 cm
Colour:	Pink and cream dress and flowers
Issued:	Jan. 1993 in a limited edition of 1,950

PRICING DATA	U.K. £	U.S. $	Can. $
Made in U.K.	200.00	300.00	400.00

FIGURINES
FLOWER FAIRIES LIMITED EDITIONS

THE SLOE FAIRY (AUTUMN)™

TECHNICAL DATA

Model No.:	B0418
Designer:	Cicely Mary Barker
Modeller:	Glenis Devereux
Height:	7 ¾", 19.7 cm
Colour:	Lilac, beige and purple clothing
Issued:	Jan. 1999 in a limited edition of 1,950
Series:	Flower Fairies of the Seasons

PRICING DATA	U.K. £	U.S. $	Can. $
Made in U.K.	170.00	—	—

THE STRAWBERRY FAIRY™

TECHNICAL DATA

Model No.:	B0115
Designer:	Cicely Mary Barker
Modeller:	Glenis Devereux
Height:	7 ¼", 18.4 cm
Colour:	Red strawberries and dress; white sleeves and wings; green leaves
Issued:	Jan. 1997 in a limited edition of 1,950

PRICING DATA	U.K. £	U.S. $	Can. $
Made in U.K.	125.00	200.00	275.00

THE WALLFLOWER FAIRY™

TECHNICAL DATA

Model No.:	CF27
Designer:	Cicely Mary Barker
Modeller:	Glenis Devereux
Height:	7 ½", 19.1 cm
Colour:	Rust and yellow clothing
Issued:	Jan. 1995 in a limited edition of 1,950

PRICING DATA	U.K. £	U.S. $	Can. $
Made in U.K.	175.00	275.00	375.00

FIGURINES
FLOWER FAIRIES LIMITED EDITIONS

THE WHITE BINDWEED FAIRY™

TECHNICAL DATA

Model No.:	CF26
Designer:	Cicely Mary Barker
Modeller:	Glenis Devereux
Height:	5 ½", 14.0 cm
Colour:	Pink dress and wings; white flowers
Issued:	Jan. 1995 in a limited edition of 1,950

PRICING DATA	U.K. £	U.S. $	Can. $
Made in U.K.	175.00	275.00	375.00

THE WILD CHERRY FAIRY™

TECHNICAL DATA

Model No.:	CF25
Designer:	Cicely Mary Barker
Modeller:	Glenis Devereux
Height:	8", 20.3 cm
Colour:	White and red dress; white flowers
Issued:	Jan. 1994 in a limited edition of 1,950

PRICING DATA	U.K. £	U.S. $	Can. $
Made in U.K.	200.00	300.00	400.00

FIGURINES
MINIATURE FAIRIES

THE APPLE BLOSSOM FAIRY™
Style Two

TECHNICAL DATA

Model No.:	726958
Designer:	Cicely Mary Barker
Modeller:	Unknown
Height:	4 ½", 11.9 cm
Colour:	Green and pink clothing; pink flowers
Issued:	Jan. 2000 to the present

PRICING DATA	U.K. £	U.S. $	Can. $
Made Abroad	24.00	—	—

THE CANDYTUFT FAIRY™
Style Two

TECHNICAL DATA

Model No.:	726974
Designer:	Cicely Mary Barker
Modeller:	Unknown
Height:	4", 10.1 cm
Colour:	Pink clothing and wings
Issued:	Jan. 2000 to the present

PRICING DATA	U.K. £	U.S. $	Can. $
Made Abroad	19.00	—	—

THE GERANIUM FAIRY™

TECHNICAL DATA

Model No.:	726923
Designer:	Cicely Mary Barker
Modeller:	Unknown
Height:	4 ½", 11.9 cm
Colour:	Green and peach dress, flowers and leaves
Issued:	Jan. 2000 to the present

PRICING DATA	U.K. £	U.S. $	Can. $
Made Abroad	19.00	—	—

FIGURINES
MINIATURE FAIRIES

THE LAVENDER FAIRY™
Style Two

TECHNICAL DATA

Model No.:	726915
Designer:	Cicely Mary Barker
Modeller:	Unknown
Height:	6", 15.0 cm
Colour:	Lilac and green dress; cream and lilac wings; lilac flowers
Issued:	Jan. 2000 to the present

PRICING DATA	U.K. £	U.S. $	Can. $
Made Abroad	19.00	—	—

THE ROSE FAIRY™
Style Two

TECHNICAL DATA

Model No.:	726966
Designer:	Cicely Mary Barker
Modeller:	Unknown
Height:	4 ¾", 12.1 cm
Colour:	Pink dress, rose and wings
Issued:	Jan. 2000 to the present

PRICING DATA	U.K. £	U.S. $	Can. $
Made Abroad	19.00	—	—

THE SWEET PEA FAIRY™
Style Two

TECHNICAL DATA

Model No.:	726931
Designer:	Cicely Mary Barker
Modeller:	Unknown
Height:	5", 12.7 cm
Colour:	Lilac, pink and green
Issued:	Jan. 2000 to the present

PRICING DATA	U.K. £	U.S. $	Can. $
Made Abroad	24.00	—	—

FIGURINES
FAIRIES BY LINDA PAGETT

FAIRY AND FROG™

TECHNICAL DATA

Model No.:	F2
Designer:	Linda Pagett
Modeller:	David Geenty
Height:	6", 15.0 cm
Colour:	Pink dress and cap; yellow-brown frog; green lilypad
Issued:	Jan. 1981-Dec. 1982

PRICING DATA	U.K. £	U.S. $	Can. $
Made in U.K.	50.00	80.00	110.00

FAIRY AND MUSHROOM™

TECHNICAL DATA

Model No.:	F3
Designer:	Linda Pagett
Modeller:	David Geenty
Height:	5", 12.7 cm
Colour:	Yellow dress; beige mushroom with brown cap
Issued:	Jan. 1981-Dec. 1982

PRICING DATA	U.K. £	U.S. $	Can. $
Made in U.K.	40.00	65.00	85.00

FAIRY AND PIPE™

TECHNICAL DATA

Model No.:	F4
Designer:	Linda Pagett
Modeller:	David Geenty
Height:	4", 10.1 cm
Colour:	Lilac outfit and cap; cream wings
Issued:	Jan. 1981-Dec. 1982

PRICING DATA	U.K. £	U.S. $	Can. $
Made in U.K.	40.00	65.00	85.00

FIGURINES
FAIRIES BY LINDA PAGETT

FAIRY AND POPPY™

TECHNICAL DATA

Model No.:	F1
Designer:	Linda Pagett
Modeller:	David Geenty
Height:	4 ½", 11.9 cm
Colour:	Yellow outfit and flower; cream wings; green leaves
Issued:	Jan. 1981-Dec. 1982

PRICING DATA	U.K. £	U.S. $	Can. $
Made in U.K.	50.00	80.00	110.00

LEGEND OF KING ARTHUR

FIGURINES

GUINEVERE™

TECHNICAL DATA

Model No.: KA02
Modeller: Mark Newman
Height: 9", 22.9 cm
Colour: Lilac dress; yellow cloak; brown hair; gold crown
Issued: Jan. 1991-Dec. 1993

PRICING DATA	U.K. £	U.S. $	Can. $
Made in U.K.	100.00	150.00	200.00

KING ARTHUR™

TECHNICAL DATA

Model No.: KA01
Modeller: Mark Newman
Height: 9 ½", 24.0 cm
Colour: Grey armour; purple cloak; silver sword; gold crown; blonde hair
Issued: Jan. 1991-Dec. 1993

PRICING DATA	U.K. £	U.S. $	Can. $
Made in U.K.	125.00	200.00	275.00

MERLIN™

TECHNICAL DATA

Model No.: KA03
Modeller: Mark Newman
Height: 9", 22.9 cm
Colour: Dark green robe; orange, tan and brown cloak; grey beard; brown and white owl
Issued: Jan. 1991-Dec. 1993

PRICING DATA	U.K. £	U.S. $	Can. $
Made in U.K.	125.00	200.00	275.00

FIGURINES

MORDRED™

TECHNICAL DATA

Model No.:	KA07
Modeller:	Mark Newman
Height:	7 ½", 19.1 cm
Colour:	Grey armour; orange shirt; tan cloak; brown hair and beard
Issued:	Jan. 1991-Dec. 1993

PRICING DATA	U.K. £	U.S. $	Can. $
Made in U.K.	125.00	200.00	275.00

MORGAN LE FAY™

TECHNICAL DATA

Model No.:	KA08
Modeller:	Mark Newman
Height:	9", 22.9 cm
Colour:	Yellow skirt; pale blue shirt; green cloak; pink headdress; strawberry blonde hair
Issued:	Jan. 1991-Dec. 1993

PRICING DATA	U.K. £	U.S. $	Can. $
Made in U.K.	100.00	150.00	200.00

SIR GALAHAD™

TECHNICAL DATA

Model No.:	KA05
Modeller:	Mark Newman
Height:	8 ½", 21.6 cm
Colour:	Grey armour; pale green cloak
Issued:	Jan. 1991-Dec. 1993

PRICING DATA	U.K. £	U.S. $	Can. $
Made in U.K.	125.00	200.00	275.00

FAIRIES

Lavender Fairy, Style One

Candytuft Fairy, Style One

Apple Blossom Fairy, Style One

Sweet Pea Fairy, Style One

FAIRIES

Nasturtium Fairy

Fuchsia Fairy

Columbine Fairy

Bugle Fairy

THELWELL™

Pony Not Yet Broken

The Lone Stranger

A Well Handled Pony

Four Hooves For Christmas

THELWELL™

The Greatest

Starting Point

Four Faults

Among The Prizes

THELWELL™

Party Time (Christmas)

Danger Point

Penelope Carolling

Halloa Away

THELWELL™

Easy Jumps First

The Picnic

It Should Be Clearly Understood Who's Boss

Fat Ponies Are Hard On The Legs

THELWELL™

Roomy Jodhpurs Are Advisable

Ponies Are Incredibly Sensitive

Never Use Spurs

No More Than Three Refusals Are Permitted

OLIVER OTTER AND FRIENDS™

Digsby The Mole

Drew The Shrew

Oliver Otter

Will Squirrel

FIGURINES

SIR GAWAINE™

TECHNICAL DATA

Model No.:	KA06
Modeller:	Mark Newman
Height:	9", 22.9 cm
Colour:	Grey armour; light brown cloak; grey moustache
Issued:	Jan. 1991-Dec. 1993

PRICING DATA	U.K. £	U.S. $	Can. $
Made in U.K.	125.00	200.00	275.00

SIR LANCELOT™

TECHNICAL DATA

Model No.:	KA04
Modeller:	Mark Newman
Height:	9 ½", 24.0 cm
Colour:	Golden armour; grey cloak; silver sword and shield
Issued:	Jan. 1991-Dec. 1993

PRICING DATA	U.K. £	U.S. $	Can. $
Made in U.K.	150.00	250.00	325.00

OLIVER OTTER
AND FRIENDS

FIGURINES

DIGSBY THE MOLE™

TECHNICAL DATA

Model No.: 330825
Designer: Kate Veale
Modeller: Richard Wawrzesta
Height: 3 ½", 8.9 cm
Colour: Brown mole; red vest
and strawberries;
blue and white bowl
Issued: June 1997-Dec. 1998

PRICING DATA	U.K. £	U.S. $	Can. $
Made Abroad	20.00	35.00	50.00

DREW THE SHREW™

TECHNICAL DATA

Model No.: 330787
Designer: Kate Veale
Modeller: Richard Wawrzesta
Height: 2 ¾", 7.0 cm
Colour: Brown shrew; white
shirt with red ladybugs;
blue sneakers; blue and
white bowl
Issued: June 1997-Dec. 1998

PRICING DATA	U.K. £	U.S. $	Can. $
Made Abroad	20.00	35.00	50.00

OLIVER OTTER™

TECHNICAL DATA

Model No.: 330809
Designer: Kate Veale
Modeller: Richard Wawrzesta
Height: 4 ½", 11.9 cm
Colour: Brown and white otter;
white shirt with heart
and fish; blue sandals;
orange bottles
Issued: June 1997-Dec. 1998

PRICING DATA	U.K. £	U.S. $	Can. $
Made Abroad	20.00	35.00	50.00

FIGURINES

WILL SQUIRREL™

TECHNICAL DATA

Model No.:	330817
Designer:	Kate Veale
Modeller:	Richard Wawrzesta
Height:	4 ¼", 10.8 cm
Colour:	Brown and white squirrel; blue shirt; white and blue lunchbox
Issued:	June 1997-Dec. 1998

PRICING DATA	U.K. £	U.S. $	Can. $
Made Abroad	20.00	35.00	50.00

BOOKENDS

OLIVER OTTER™ BOOKENDS

TECHNICAL DATA

Model No.:	330833
Designer:	Kate Veale
Modeller:	Richard Wawrzesta
Height:	5", 12.7 cm
Colour:	Brown, red, white, blue and green
Issued:	June 1997-Dec. 1998

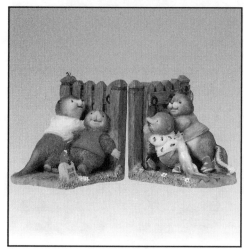

PRICING DATA	U.K. £	U.S. $	Can. $
Made Abroad	60.00	100.00	125.00

CLOCKS

OLIVER OTTER™ SUNFLOWER CLOCK

TECHNICAL DATA

Model No.:	330795
Designer:	Kate Veale
Modeller:	Richard Wawrzesta
Height:	7 ¾", 19.7 cm
Colour:	Brown, blue, white, green and yellow
Issued:	June 1997-Dec. 1998

PRICING DATA	U.K. £	U.S. $	Can. $
Made Abroad	50.00	80.00	100.00

PETER PAN

FIGURINES

CROCODILE™

TECHNICAL DATA

Model No.:	PP06
Modeller:	Glenis Devereux
Height:	1 ½", 3.8 cm
Colour:	Green body; pink tongue
Issued:	July 1994-Dec. 1995

PRICING DATA	U.K. £	U.S. $	Can. $
Made in U.K.	25.00	35.00	50.00

HOOK™

TECHNICAL DATA

Model No.:	PP04
Modeller:	Glenis Devereux
Height:	6 ½", 16.5 cm
Colour:	Cream shirt; red vest and belt; grey pantaloons and sword; black hat with white plume
Issued:	July 1994-Dec. 1995

PRICING DATA	U.K. £	U.S. $	Can. $
Made in U.K.	50.00	80.00	100.00

PETER PAN™

TECHNICAL DATA

Model No.:	PP01
Modeller:	Glenis Devereux
Height:	5", 12.7 cm
Colour:	Green clothing and shoes: black hat with red band
Issued:	July 1994-Dec. 1995

PRICING DATA	U.K. £	U.S. $	Can. $
Made in U.K.	40.00	65.00	90.00

FIGURINES

SMEE™

TECHNICAL DATA

Model No.:	PP05
Modeller:	Glenis Devereux
Height:	3", 7.6 cm
Colour:	Blue and white striped clothing; red neckerchief; black shoes with gold buckles
Issued:	July 1994-Dec. 1995

PRICING DATA	U.K. £	U.S. $	Can. $
Made in U.K.	25.00	35.00	50.00

TINKER BELL™

TECHNICAL DATA

Model No.:	PP03
Modeller:	Glenis Devereux
Height:	4 ¾", 12.1 cm
Colour:	Lilac frock with gold bells; brown and beige mushroom
Issued:	July 1994-Dec. 1995

PRICING DATA	U.K. £	U.S. $	Can. $
Made in U.K.	35.00	60.00	80.00

WENDY™

TECHNICAL DATA

Model No.:	PP02
Modeller:	Glenis Devereux
Height:	5 ¾", 14.6 cm
Colour:	Pink frock; blue kite; tan rope with pink bows
Issued:	July 1994-Dec. 1995

PRICING DATA	U.K. £	U.S. $	Can. $
Made in U.K.	45.00	75.00	100.00

RUFF & REDDY

FIGURINES

HELPING HANDS

TECHNICAL DATA

Model No.:	RR05
Modeller:	Anne Wall
Height:	4", 10.1 cm
Colour:	Black and white collie; ginger cat; grey tool box
Issued:	Jan. 1995-Dec. 1999

PRICING DATA	U.K. £	U.S. $	Can. $
Made in U.K.	45.00	75.00	100.00

HEN PECKED

TECHNICAL DATA

Model No.:	RR06
Modeller:	Anne Wall
Height:	3 ½", 8.9 cm
Colour:	Black and white collie; ginger cat; white and black hen; white feed bowl
Issued:	Jan. 1995 to the present

PRICING DATA	U.K. £	U.S. $	Can. $
Made in U.K.	44.95	—	—

HIDE AND SEEK

TECHNICAL DATA

Model No.:	RR08
Modeller:	Anne Wall
Height:	3 ¼", 8.3 cm
Colour:	Black and white collie; ginger cat in grey pail
Issued:	Jan. 1996-Dec. 1999

PRICING DATA	U.K. £	U.S. $	Can. $
Made in U.K.	40.00	75.00	100.00

FIGURINES

HIGH JINKS

TECHNICAL DATA

Model No.:	RR03
Modeller:	Anne Wall
Height:	5 ½", 14.0 cm
Colour:	Black and white collie; ginger cat; brown tree stump
Issued:	Jan. 1995 to the present

PRICING DATA	U.K. £	U.S. $	Can. $
Made in U.K.	45.00	—	—

IF THE CAP FITS

TECHNICAL DATA

Model No.:	RR07
Modeller:	Anne Wall
Height:	3 ¾", 9.5 cm
Colour:	Black and white collie wearing cloth cap; ginger cat
Issued:	Jan. 1996-Dec. 1997

PRICING DATA	U.K. £	U.S. $	Can. $
Made in U.K.	40.00	65.00	85.00

NOT MY SIZE

TECHNICAL DATA

Model No.:	RR02
Modeller:	Anne Wall
Height:	3 ¾", 9.5 cm
Colour:	Black and white collie; ginger cat with dark grey wellingtons
Issued:	Jan. 1995 to the present

PRICING DATA	U.K. £	U.S. $	Can. $
Made in U.K.	42.00	—	—

FIGURINES

SCARECROW SCALLYWAGS

TECHNICAL DATA

Model No.: BO085
Modeller: Anne Wall
Height: 6 ¾", 17.2 cm
Colour: Black and white collie; ginger cat; scarecrow wears brown and blue clothing
Issued: Jan. 1997-June 1999

PRICING DATA	U.K. £	U.S. $	Can. $
Made in U.K.	50.00	80.00	100.00

TAKING THE BISCUIT

TECHNICAL DATA

Model No.: BO295
Modeller: Anne Wall
Height: 5 ½", 14.0 cm
Colour: Black and white collie; ginger cat; beige sacks
Issued: June 1998 to the present

PRICING DATA	U.K. £	U.S. $	Can. $
Made in U.K.	52.00	—	—

TYRED OUT

TECHNICAL DATA

Model No.: RR01
Modeller: Anne Wall
Height: 2 ¾", 7.0 cm
Colour: Black and white collie; ginger cat in a black tyre
Issued: Jan. 1995-Dec. 1997

PRICING DATA	U.K. £	U.S. $	Can. $
Made in U.K.	40.00	65.00	85.00

FIGURINES

WASHDAY BLUES

TECHNICAL DATA

Model No.:	RR04
Modeller:	Anne Wall
Height:	3", 7.6 cm
Colour:	Black and white collie; ginger cat; blue dungarees
Issued:	Jan. 1995-June 1999

PRICING DATA	U.K. £	U.S. $	Can. $
Made in U.K.	40.00	65.00	85.00

THELWELL

Thelwell's Riding Academy
Thelwell Goes West

FIGURINES
THELWELL'S RIDING ACADEMY

A WELL HANDLED PONY™

TECHNICAL DATA

Model No.:	T15
Modeller:	Fred Moore
Height:	3", 7.6 cm
Colour:	1. Bay; red, green, blue and tan clothing
	2. Grey; red, green, blue and tan clothing
Issued:	1987-Dec. 1989

PRICING DATA	U.K. £	U.S. $	Can. $
Made in U.K.	35.00	55.00	75.00

AMONG THE PRIZES™

TECHNICAL DATA

Model No.:	T35
Modeller:	Richard Wawrzesta
Height:	3", 7.6 cm
Colour:	1. Bay; maroon and cream clothing
	2. Grey; maroon and cream clothing
Issued:	June 1991-Dec. 1993

PRICING DATA	U.K. £	U.S. $	Can. $
Made in U.K.	35.00	55.00	75.00

BOILING POINT™

TECHNICAL DATA

Model No.:	T48
Modeller:	Richard Wawrzesta
Height:	2 ¼", 5.7 cm
Colour:	1. Bay; blue and cream clothing
	2. Grey; blue and cream clothing
Issued:	July 1992-Dec. 1993

PRICING DATA	U.K. £	U.S. $	Can. $
Made in U.K.	50.00	80.00	100.00

FIGURINES
THELWELL'S RIDING ACADEMY

BRUSH VIGOROUSLY - HE'LL ENJOY IT™

TECHNICAL DATA

Model No.:	T10/140-709
Modeller:	Fred Moore
Height:	2 ½", 6.4 cm
Colour:	1. Bay; green jacket; brown brush
	2. Grey; green jacket; brown brush
Issued:	1985-Dec. 1993

PRICING DATA	U.K. £	U.S. $	Can. $
Made in U.K.	25.00	40.00	60.00

CHRISTMAS DELIVERY™
Style One

TECHNICAL DATA

Model No.:	T22
Modeller:	Fred Moore
Height:	3", 7.6 cm
Colour:	1. Bay; red clothing; multi-coloured packages
	2. Grey: red clothing; multi-coloured packages
Issued:	Dec. 1988-Dec. 1989

PRICING DATA	U.K. £	U.S. $	Can. $
Made in U.K.	50.00	80.00	100.00

CHRISTMAS DELIVERY™
Style Two

TECHNICAL DATA

Model No.:	T53
Modeller:	Richard Wawrzesta
Height:	3 ¼", 8.3 cm
Colour:	1. Bay; red clothing; multi-coloured packages
	2. Grey; red clothing; multi-coloured packages
Issued:	Jan. 1994-Dec. 1994

PRICING DATA	U.K. £	U.S. $	Can. $
Made in U.K.	50.00	80.00	100.00

FIGURINES
THELWELL'S RIDING ACADEMY

CHRISTMAS FAIRY™

TECHNICAL DATA

Model No.: T46
Modeller: Richard Wawrzesta
Height: 2 ½", 6.4 cm
Colour: 1. Bay; red and green clothing
2. Grey; red and green clothing
Issued: July 1992-Dec. 1993

PRICING DATA	U.K. £	U.S. $	Can. $
Made in U.K.	50.00	80.00	100.00

CHRISTMAS PARTY™

TECHNICAL DATA

Model No.: T50
Modeller: Richard Wawrzesta
Height: 2 ½", 6.4 cm
Colour: 1. Bay; blue and cream clothing; orange carrot
2. Grey; blue and cream clothing; orange carrot
Issued: July 1993-Dec. 1993

PRICING DATA	U.K. £	U.S. $	Can. $
Made in U.K.	75.00	125.00	175.00

CHRISTMAS TREAT™

TECHNICAL DATA

Model No.: T11
Modeller: Fred Moore
Height: 3", 7.6 cm
Colour: 1. Bay; blue, rose and cream clothing
2. Grey; blue, rose and cream clothing
Issued: Dec. 1985-Dec. 1986

PRICING DATA	U.K. £	U.S. $	Can. $
Made in U.K.	50.00	80.00	100.00

FIGURINES
THELWELL'S RIDING ACADEMY

DANGER POINT™

TECHNICAL DATA

Model No.:	T49
Modeller:	Richard Wawrzesta
Height:	2 ¾", 7.0 cm
Colour:	1. Bay; red and cream clothing
	2. Grey; red and cream clothing
Issued:	July 1992-Dec. 1993

PRICING DATA	U.K. £	U.S. $	Can. $
Made in U.K.	45.00	75.00	100.00

DON'T EXPECT HIM TO READ YOUR MIND™

TECHNICAL DATA

Model No.:	T55
Modeller:	Richard Wawrzesta
Height:	2 ½", 6.4 cm
Colour:	1. Bay; red and cream clothing
	2. Grey; red and cream clothing
Issued:	Jan. 1995-Dec. 1995

PRICING DATA	U.K. £	U.S. $	Can. $
Made in U.K.	75.00	125.00	175.00

DON'T PANIC OVER HIS SIMPLE AILMENTS™

TECHNICAL DATA

Model No.:	T9/140-708
Modeller:	Fred Moore
Height:	3", 7.6 cm
Colour:	1. Bay; white coat; brown stethoscope
	2. Grey; white coat; brown stethoscope
Issued:	1985-Dec. 1989

PRICING DATA	U.K. £	U.S. $	Can. $
Made in U.K.	30.00	50.00	75.00

FIGURINES
THELWELL'S RIDING ACADEMY

DON'T PLAY WITH YOUR PONY IN THE GARDEN™

TECHNICAL DATA

Model No.:	T24
Modeller:	Richard Wawrzesta
Height:	3", 7.6 cm
Colour:	1. Bay; red jacket; yellow, red and blue flowers
	2. Grey; red jacket; yellow, red and blue flowers
Issued:	Dec. 1989-Dec. 1993

PRICING DATA	U.K. £	U.S. $	Can. $
Made in U.K.	30.00	50.00	75.00

DON'T TIRE YOUR PONY™

TECHNICAL DATA

Model No.:	T1/140-706
Modeller:	Fred Moore
Height:	2", 5.0 cm
Colour:	1. Bay; tan and cream clothing
	2. Grey; tan and cream clothing
Issued:	1984-Dec. 1989

PRICING DATA	U.K. £	U.S. $	Can. $
Made in U.K.	25.00	40.00	60.00

EASY JUMPS FIRST™

TECHNICAL DATA

Model No.:	T13
Modeller:	Fred Moore
Height:	3", 7.6 cm
Colour:	1. Bay; tan, blue and cream clothing
	2. Grey; tan, blue and cream clothing
Issued:	1986-Dec. 1993

PRICING DATA	U.K. £	U.S. $	Can. $
Made in U.K.	20.00	35.00	45.00

FIGURINES
THELWELL'S RIDING ACADEMY

FAT PONIES ARE HARD ON THE LEGS™

TECHNICAL DATA

Model No.:	T52
Modeller:	Richard Wawrzesta
Height:	2 ½", 6.4 cm
Colour:	1. Bay; red and cream clothing
	2. Grey; red and cream clothing
Issued:	July 1993-Dec. 1993

PRICING DATA	U.K. £	U.S. $	Can. $
Made in U.K.	75.00	125.00	175.00

FOUR FAULTS™

TECHNICAL DATA

Model No.:	T8/140-707
Modeller:	Fred Moore
Height:	3", 7.6 cm
Colour:	1. Bay; blue and cream clothing; red, blue and yellow flowers
	2. Grey; blue and cream clothing; red, blue and yellow flowers
Issued:	1985-Dec. 1993

PRICING DATA	U.K. £	U.S. $	Can. $
Made in U.K.	20.00	35.00	45.00

FOUR HOOVES FOR CHRISTMAS™

TECHNICAL DATA

Model No.:	T25
Modeller:	Richard Wawrzesta
Height:	3", 7.6 cm
Colour:	1. Bay; maroon and cream clothing
	2. Grey; maroon and cream clothing
Issued:	Dec. 1989-Dec. 1991

PRICING DATA	U.K. £	U.S. $	Can. $
Made in U.K.	35.00	55.00	75.00

FIGURINES
THELWELL'S RIDING ACADEMY

THE GARDENERS™

TECHNICAL DATA

Model No.:	T36
Modeller:	Richard Wawrzesta
Height:	2 ½", 6.4 cm
Colour:	1. Bay; red, tan and cream clothing
	2. Grey; red, tan and cream clothing
Issued:	June 1991-Dec. 1993

PRICING DATA	U.K. £	U.S. $	Can. $
Made in U.K.	35.00	55.00	75.00

GOOD MANNERS ARE ESSENTIAL IN A PONY™

TECHNICAL DATA

Model No.:	T18
Modeller:	Fred Moore
Height:	2", 5.0 cm
Colour:	1. Bay; blue and cream clothing; grey fence
	2. Grey; blue and cream clothing; grey fence
Issued:	1987-Dec. 1993

PRICING DATA	U.K. £	U.S. $	Can. $
Made in U.K.	25.00	40.00	60.00

THE GREATEST™

TECHNICAL DATA

Model No.:	T5/140-702
Modeller:	Fred Moore
Height:	3", 7.6 cm
Colour:	1. Bay; burgundy and cream clothing
	2. Grey; burgundy and cream clothing
Issued:	1984-Dec. 1993

PRICING DATA	U.K. £	U.S. $	Can. $
Made in U.K.	20.00	35.00	45.00

FIGURINES
THELWELL'S RIDING ACADEMY

GROOM DAILY™

TECHNICAL DATA

Model No.:	T12
Modeller:	Fred Moore
Height:	3", 7.6 cm
Colour:	1. Bay; tan and cream clothing; grey pail
	2. Grey; tan and cream clothing; grey pail
Issued:	1986-Dec. 1993

PRICING DATA	U.K. £	U.S. $	Can. $
Made in U.K.	20.00	35.00	45.00

HALLOA AWAY™

TECHNICAL DATA

Model No.:	T7/140-701
Modeller:	Fred Moore
Height:	3", 7.6 cm
Colour:	1. Bay; red and cream clothing; brown fox
	2. Grey; red and cream clothing; brown fox
Issued:	1985-Dec. 1993

PRICING DATA	U.K. £	U.S. $	Can. $
Made in U.K.	20.00	35.00	45.00

HE'LL FIND YOU™

TECHNICAL DATA

Model No.:	T3/140-704
Modeller:	Fred Moore
Height:	3", 7.6 cm
Colour:	1. Bay; green and cream clothing
	2. Grey; green and cream clothing
Issued:	1984-Dec. 1993

PRICING DATA	U.K. £	U.S. $	Can. $
Made in U.K.	20.00	35.00	45.00

FIGURINES
THELWELL'S RIDING ACADEMY

IN A DEEP DRIFT™

TECHNICAL DATA

Model No.:	T19
Modeller:	Fred Moore
Height:	3", 7.6 cm
Colour:	1. Bay; green and cream clothing; brown log
	2. Grey; green and cream clothing; brown log
Issued:	1987-Dec. 1989

PRICING DATA	U.K. £	U.S. $	Can. $
Made in U.K.	35.00	55.00	75.00

IT SHOULD BE CLEARLY UNDERSTOOD WHO'S BOSS™

TECHNICAL DATA

Model No.:	T23
Modeller:	Richard Wawrzesta
Height:	3", 7.6 cm
Colour:	1. Bay; green and cream clothing
	2. Grey; green and cream clothing
Issued:	Dec. 1989-Dec. 1993

PRICING DATA	U.K. £	U.S. $	Can. $
Made in U.K.	30.00	50.00	75.00

NEVER USE SPURS™

TECHNICAL DATA

Model No.:	T51
Modeller:	Richard Wawrzesta
Height:	2 ¼", 7.0 cm
Colour:	1. Bay; red and cream clothing
	2. Grey; red and cream clothing
Issued:	July 1993-Dec. 1993

PRICING DATA	U.K. £	U.S. $	Can. $
Made in U.K.	75.00	125.00	175.00

FIGURINES
THELWELL'S RIDING ACADEMY

THE NIGHT BEFORE CHRISTMAS™

TECHNICAL DATA

Model No.:	T26
Modeller:	Richard Wawrzesta
Height:	1 ½", 3.8 cm
Colour:	1. Bay; red and cream clothing
	2. Grey; red and cream clothing
Issued:	July 1990-Dec. 1991

PRICING DATA	U.K. £	U.S. $	Can. $
Made in U.K.	50.00	80.00	100.00

NO MORE THAN THREE REFUSALS ARE PERMITTED™

TECHNICAL DATA

Model No.:	T28
Modeller:	Richard Wawrzesta
Height:	2 ¾", 7.0 cm
Colour:	1. Bay; blue and cream clothing
	2. Grey; blue and cream clothing
Issued:	July 1990-Dec. 1993

PRICING DATA	U.K. £	U.S. $	Can. $
Made in U.K.	30.00	50.00	75.00

PARTY TIME (Christmas)™

TECHNICAL DATA

Model No.:	T14
Modeller:	Fred Moore
Height:	3", 7.6 cm
Colour:	1. Bay; red and cream clothing; yellow and orange party hats
	2. Grey; red and cream clothing; yellow and orange party hats
Issued:	Dec. 1986-Dec. 1989

PRICING DATA	U.K. £	U.S. $	Can. $
Made in U.K.	30.00	50.00	75.00

FIGURINES
THELWELL'S RIDING ACADEMY

PENELOPE CAROLLING™

TECHNICAL DATA

Model No.:	T6
Modeller:	Fred Moore
Height:	2 ¾", 7.0 cm
Colour:	1. Bay; orange, red and cream clothing
	2. Grey; orange, red and cream clothing
Issued:	Dec. 1984-Dec. 1985

PRICING DATA	U.K. £	U.S. $	Can. $
Made in U.K.	50.00	80.00	100.00

THE PICNIC™

TECHNICAL DATA

Model No.:	T27
Modeller:	Richard Wawrzesta
Height:	2 ¼", 5.7 cm
Colour:	1. Bay; green and cream clothing
	2. Grey; green and cream clothing
Issued:	July 1990-Dec. 1993

PRICING DATA	U.K. £	U.S. $	Can. $
Made in U.K.	30.00	50.00	75.00

POINT OF DEPARTURE™

TECHNICAL DATA

Model No.:	T4/140-703
Modeller:	Fred Moore
Height:	3", 7.6 cm
Colour:	1. Bay; red and cream clothing
	2. Grey; red and cream clothing
Issued:	1984-Dec. 1993

PRICING DATA	U.K. £	U.S. $	Can. $
Made in U.K.	20.00	35.00	45.00

FIGURINES
THELWELL'S RIDING ACADEMY

PONIES ARE INCREDIBLY SENSITIVE™

TECHNICAL DATA

Model No.:	T29
Modeller:	Richard Wawrzesta
Height:	2 ½", 6.4 cm
Colour:	1. Bay; blue and cream clothing
	2. Grey; blue and cream clothing
Issued:	June 1991-Dec. 1993

PRICING DATA	U.K. £	U.S. $	Can. $
Made in U.K.	35.00	55.00	75.00

PONY NOT YET BROKEN™

TECHNICAL DATA

Model No.:	T17
Modeller:	Fred Moore
Height:	3", 7.6 cm
Colour:	1. Bay; green, blue and red clothing
	2. Grey; green, blue and red clothing
Issued:	1987-Dec. 1993

PRICING DATA	U.K. £	U.S. $	Can. $
Made in U.K.	25.00	40.00	60.00

REMEMBER TO PRAISE HIM™

TECHNICAL DATA

Model No.:	T20
Modeller:	Fred Moore
Height:	3", 7.6 cm
Colour:	1. Bay; red jacket; blue and red ribbons; silver cup
	2. Grey; red jacket; blue and red ribbons; silver cup
Issued:	Dec. 1988-Dec. 1993

PRICING DATA	U.K. £	U.S. $	Can. $
Made in U.K.	25.00	40.00	60.00

FIGURINES
THELWELL'S RIDING ACADEMY

ROOMY JODHPURS ARE ADVISABLE™

TECHNICAL DATA

Model No.:	T21
Modeller:	Fred Moore
Height:	3", 7.6 cm
Colour:	1. Bay; maroon and cream clothing
	2. Grey; maroon and cream clothing
Issued:	Dec. 1988-Dec. 1993

PRICING DATA	U.K. £	U.S. $	Can. $
Made in U.K.	25.00	40.00	60.00

STARTING POINT™

TECHNICAL DATA

Model No.:	T47
Modeller:	Richard Wawrzesta
Height:	3", 7.6 cm
Colour:	1. Bay; maroon and cream clothing
	2. Grey; maroon and cream clothing
Issued:	July 1992-Dec. 1993

PRICING DATA	U.K. £	U.S. $	Can. $
Made in U.K.	50.00	80.00	100.00

TALK TO YOUR PONY™

TECHNICAL DATA

Model No.:	T2/140-705
Modeller:	Fred Moore
Height:	2 ½", 6.4 cm
Colour:	1. Bay; blue and cream clothing
	2. Grey; blue and cream clothing
Issued:	1984-Dec. 1993

PRICING DATA	U.K. £	U.S. $	Can. $
Made in U.K.	20.00	35.00	45.00

FIGURINES
THELWELL'S RIDING ACADEMY

TREAT YOUR PONY AS YOU LIKE TO BE TREATED YOURSELF™

TECHNICAL DATA

Model No.:	T16
Modeller:	Fred Moore
Height:	2 ½", 6.4 cm
Colour:	1. Bay; blue and cream clothing; red scarf
	2. Grey; blue and cream clothing; red scarf
Issued:	1987-Dec. 1993

PRICING DATA	U.K. £	U.S. $	Can. $
Made in U.K.	25.00	40.00	60.00

WINTER SPORTS™

TECHNICAL DATA

Model No.:	T37
Modeller:	Richard Wawrzesta
Height:	3", 7.6 cm
Colour:	1. Bay; red, blue, green and cream clothing
	2. Grey; red, blue, green and cream clothing
Issued:	June 1991-Dec. 1993

PRICING DATA	U.K. £	U.S. $	Can. $
Made in U.K.	35.00	55.00	75.00

YOU'LL HAVE TO WAIT FOR CHRISTMAS™

TECHNICAL DATA

Model No.:	T54
Modeller:	Richard Wawrzesta
Height:	2 ½", 6.4 cm
Colour:	1. Bay; green tree; blue jacket
	2. Grey; green tree; blue jacket
Issued:	Jan. 1995-Dec. 1995

PRICING DATA	U.K. £	U.S. $	Can. $
Made in U.K.	50.00	80.00	100.00

TRINKET BOXES
THELWELL'S RIDING ACADEMY

DON'T TIRE YOUR PONY™

TECHNICAL DATA

Model No.:	T30
Modeller:	Richard Wawrzesta
Height:	3 ¼", 8.3 cm
Colour:	1. Bay; red and cream clothing
	2. Grey; red and cream clothing
Issued:	Jan. 1989-Dec. 1993

PRICING DATA	U.K. £	U.S. $	Can. $
Made in U.K.	35.00	55.00	75.00

EASY JUMPS FIRST™

TECHNICAL DATA

Model No.:	T34
Modeller:	Richard Wawrzesta
Height:	3 ¾", 9.5 cm
Colour:	1. Bay; blue, rose-pink and cream clothing
	2. Grey; blue, rose-pink and cream clothing
Issued:	Jan. 1989-Dec. 1993

PRICING DATA	U.K. £	U.S. $	Can. $
Made in U.K.	35.00	55.00	75.00

THE GREATEST™

TECHNICAL DATA

Model No.:	T33
Modeller:	Richard Wawrzesta
Height:	4 ½", 11.9 cm
Colour:	1. Bay; red and cream clothing
	2. Grey; red and cream clothing
Issued:	Jan. 1989-Dec. 1993

PRICING DATA	U.K. £	U.S. $	Can. $
Made in U.K.	35.00	55.00	75.00

TRINKET BOXES
THELWELL'S RIDING ACADEMY

HE'LL FIND YOU™

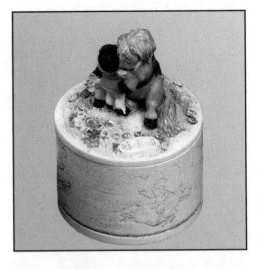

TECHNICAL DATA

Model No.:	T31
Modeller:	Richard Wawrzesta
Height:	3 ½", 8.9 cm
Colour:	1. Bay; rose-pink and cream clothing
	2. Grey; rose-pink and cream clothing
Issued:	Jan. 1989-Dec. 1993

PRICING DATA	U.K. £	U.S. $	Can. $
Made in U.K.	35.00	55.00	75.00

POINT OF DEPARTURE™

TECHNICAL DATA

Model No.:	T32
Modeller:	Richard Wawrzesta
Height:	4", 10.1 cm
Colour:	1. Bay; green and cream clothing
	2. Grey; green and cream clothing
Issued:	Jan. 1989-Dec. 1993

PRICING DATA	U.K. £	U.S. $	Can. $
Made in U.K.	35.00	55.00	75.00

FIGURINES
THELWELL GOES WEST

BRONCO BUSTER™

TECHNICAL DATA

Model No.: T43
Modeller: Richard Wawrzesta
Height: 3", 7.6 cm
Colour: 1. Bay; brown, blue and tan clothing
2. Grey; brown, blue and tan clothing
Issued: June 1991-Dec. 1993

PRICING DATA	U.K. £	U.S. $	Can. $
Made in U.K.	35.00	50.00	65.00

LEARN WHAT HE'S SAYING™

TECHNICAL DATA

Model No.: T41
Modeller: Richard Wawrzesta
Height: 2 ½", 6.4 cm
Colour: 1. Bay; tan and blue clothing
2. Grey; tan and blue clothing
Issued: June 1991-Dec. 1993

PRICING DATA	U.K. £	U.S. $	Can. $
Made in U.K.	35.00	55.00	65.00

THE LONE STRANGER™

TECHNICAL DATA

Model No.: T40
Modeller: Richard Wawrzesta
Height: 3", 7.6 cm
Colour: 1. Bay; red and blue clothing; black and white skunk
2. Grey; red and blue clothing; black and white skunk
Issued: June 1991-Dec. 1993

PRICING DATA	U.K. £	U.S. $	Can. $
Made in U.K.	35.00	50.00	65.00

FIGURINES
THELWELL GOES WEST

SMART DUDE™

TECHNICAL DATA

Model No.:	T45
Modeller:	Richard Wawrzesta
Height:	3 ½", 8.9 cm
Colour:	1. Bay; red, blue and tan clothing
	2. Grey; red. blue and tan clothing
Issued:	June 1991-Dec. 1993

PRICING DATA	U.K. £	U.S. $	Can. $
Made in U.K.	35.00	50.00	65.00

TREAT HIM LIKE A PAL™

TECHNICAL DATA

Model No.:	T44
Modeller:	Richard Wawrzesta
Height:	3", 7.6 cm
Colour:	1. Bay; black clothing
	2. Grey; black clothing
Issued:	June 1991-Dec. 1993

PRICING DATA	U.K. £	U.S. $	Can. $
Made in U.K.	35.00	50.00	65.00

TUMBLEWEED™

TECHNICAL DATA

Model No.:	T42
Modeller:	Richard Wawrzesta
Height:	3", 7.6 cm
Colour:	1. Bay; blue, brown and red clothing
	2. Bay; blue, brown and red clothing
Issued:	June 1991-Dec. 1993

PRICING DATA	U.K. £	U.S. $	Can. $
Made in U.K.	35.00	50.00	65.00

WIND IN THE WILLOWS

Border Fine Arts™

FIGURINES

BADGER™

TECHNICAL DATA

Model No.:	M33
Modeller:	David Fryer
Height:	Unknown
Colour:	Black and white; green jacket; tan trousers; brown accordion
Issued:	July 1983-Dec. 1983
Series:	Miniatures on Bronze

PRICING DATA	U.K. £	U.S. $	Can. $
Made in U.K.	50.00	80.00	100.00

MOLE™

TECHNICAL DATA

Model No.:	M31
Modeller:	David Fryer
Height:	Unknown
Colour:	Brown; yellow jacket and waistcoat; lilac trousers; red cap
Issued:	July 1983-Dec. 1983
Series:	Miniatures on Bronze

PRICING DATA	U.K. £	U.S. $	Can. $
Made in U.K.	50.00	80.00	100.00

FIGURINES

RATTY™

TECHNICAL DATA

Model No.:	M30
Modeller:	David Fryer
Height:	Unknown
Colour:	Brown; blue jacket; green trousers
Issued:	July 1983-Dec. 1983
Series:	Miniatures on Bronze

PRICING DATA	U.K. £	U.S. $	Can. $
Made in U.K.	50.00	80.00	100.00

TOAD™

TECHNICAL DATA

Model No.:	M32
Modeller:	David Fryer
Height:	Unknown
Colour:	Green; yellow jacket; blue waistcoat; lilac trousers
Issued:	July 1983-Dec. 1983
Series:	Miniatures on Bronze

PRICING DATA	U.K. £	U.S. $	Can. $
Made in U.K.	50.00	80.00	100.00

FIGURINES

EEYORE™ GETTING DRIED

TECHNICAL DATA

Model No.:	A0069
Modeller:	Richard Wawrzesta
Height:	4", 10.8 cm
Colour:	Eeyore: grey and black; Pooh: golden brown; Piglet: pink with green clothing; red, blue and white towels; green grass
Issued:	Jan. 2000 to the present

PRICING DATA	U.K. £	U.S. $	Can. $
Made Abroad	17.00	—	—

PIGLET™ CARRYING BALLOON

TECHNICAL DATA

Model No.:	A0411
Modeller:	Richard Wawrzesta
Height:	3", 7.6 cm
Colour:	Piglet: pink with green clothing; blue balloon
Issued:	June 2000 to the present

PRICING DATA	U.K. £	U.S. $	Can. $
Made Abroad	9.95	—	—

PIGLET™ WITH BALLOON

TECHNICAL DATA

Model No.:	A0060
Modeller:	Richard Wawrzesta
Height:	4", 10.8 cm
Colour:	Piglet: pink with green clothing; Pooh: golden brown; Tigger: orange with black stripes; red balloon
Issued:	Jan. 2000 to the present

PRICING DATA	U.K. £	U.S. $	Can. $
Made Abroad	18.00	—	—

FIGURINES

POOH™ AND MIRROR

TECHNICAL DATA

Model No.:	A0070
Modeller:	Richard Wawrzesta
Height:	4", 10.8 cm
Colour:	Pooh: golden brown; Piglet: pink with green clothing; silver mirror; white and red mat; brown base
Issued:	Jan. 2000 to the present

PRICING DATA	U.K. £	U.S. $	Can. $
Made Abroad	13.00	—	—

POOH™, EEYORE™ AND HUNNY

TECHNICAL DATA

Model No.:	A0063
Modeller:	Richard Wawrzesta
Height:	2 ½", 6.4 cm
Colour:	Pooh: golden brown; Eeyore: grey and black; red and brown "hunny" jars; brown base
Issued:	Jan. 2000 to the present

PRICING DATA	U.K. £	U.S. $	Can. $
Made Abroad	17.00	—	—

POOH™, HUNNY AND FOXGLOVES

TECHNICAL DATA

Model No.:	A0062
Modeller:	Richard Wawrzesta
Height:	3 ¼", 8.3 cm
Colour:	Pooh: golden brown; yellow, brown, and tan jars of "hunny"; green grass with multicoloured flowers and pink foxgloves
Issued:	Jan. 2000 to the present

PRICING DATA	U.K. £	U.S. $	Can. $
Made Abroad	16.00	—	—

FIGURINES

POOH™ LYING DOWN WITH HUNNY JAR

TECHNICAL DATA

Model No.: A0102
Modeller: Richard Wawrzesta
Height: 2 ¼", 7.0 cm
Colour: Pooh: golden brown;
brown and yellow jars
of "hunny"; green grass
Issued: Jan. 2000 to the present

PRICING DATA	U.K. £	U.S. $	Can. $
Made Abroad	9.95	—	—

POOH™, PIGLET™ AND FLOWERS

TECHNICAL DATA

Model No.: A0066
Modeller: Richard Wawrzesta
Height: 4", 10.1 cm
Colour: Pooh: golden brown;
Piglet: pink with green
clothing; red, blue and
yellow flowers; brown log;
green grass
Issued: Jan. 2000 to the present

PRICING DATA	U.K. £	U.S. $	Can. $
Made Abroad	17.00	—	—

POOH™ READING

TECHNICAL DATA

Model No.: A0065
Modeller: Richard Wawrzesta
Height: 4 ¼", 10.8 cm
Colour: Pooh: golden brown;
Piglet: pink with green
clothing; Tigger: orange
with black stripes; red,
green and blue books
Issued: Jan. 2000 to the present

PRICING DATA	U.K. £	U.S. $	Can. $
Made Abroad	18.00	—	—

FIGURINES

POOH™ SLEEPING

TECHNICAL DATA

Model No.:	A0067
Modeller:	Richard Wawrzesta
Height:	2 ¾", 7.0 cm
Colour:	Pooh: golden brown; Piglet: pink with green clothing; red armchair; white pillow; red and blue books
Issued:	Jan. 2000 to the present

PRICING DATA	U.K. £	U.S. $	Can. $
Made Abroad	16.00	—	—

POOH™ WRITING

TECHNICAL DATA

Model No.:	A0064
Modeller:	Richard Wawrzesta
Height:	2 ½", 6.4 cm
Colour:	Pooh: golden brown; white paper with black ink; grey quill; blue pot of ink
Issued:	Jan. 2000 to the present

PRICING DATA	U.K. £	U.S. $	Can. $
Made Abroad	13.00	—	—

POOH'S™ PICNIC

TECHNICAL DATA

Model No.:	A0061
Modeller:	Richard Wawrzesta
Height:	3 ¼", 8.3 cm
Colour:	Pooh: golden brown; Piglet: pink with green clothing; yellow and red jars of "hunny"; pink blanket; brown picnic basket
Issued:	Jan. 2000 to the present

PRICING DATA	U.K. £	U.S. $	Can. $
Made Abroad	18.00	—	—

FIGURINES

TIGGER™ AND BATHTUB

TECHNICAL DATA

Model No.:	A0068
Modeller:	Richard Wawrzesta
Height:	3 ½", 8.9 cm
Colour:	Tigger: orange with black stripes; Pooh: golden brown; Piglet: pink with green clothing; grey bathtub; white mat with red trim
Issued:	Jan. 2000 to the present

PRICING DATA	U.K. £	U.S. $	Can. $
Made Abroad	18.00	—	—

TIGGER™, POOH™ AND PIGLET™

TECHNICAL DATA

Model No.:	A0059
Modeller:	Richard Wawrzesta
Height:	3", 7.6 cm
Colour:	Tigger: orange with black stripes; Pooh: golden brown; Piglet: pink with green clothing; green grass with blue, yellow and red flowers
Issued:	Jan. 2000 to the present

PRICING DATA	U.K. £	U.S. $	Can. $
Made Abroad	18.00	—	—

TIGGERS™ DON'T LIKE HUNNY

TECHNICAL DATA

Model No.:	A0413
Modeller:	Richard Wawrzesta
Height:	2 ¼", 5.7 cm
Colour:	Tigger: orange with black stripes; brown and yellow pot; green grass with multicoloured flowers
Issued:	June 2000 to the present

PRICING DATA	U.K. £	U.S. $	Can. $
Made Abroad	14.00	—	—

FIGURINES

WINNIE THE POOH™ WITH HUNNY JAR

TECHNICAL DATA

Model No.:	A0412
Modeller:	Richard Wawrzesta
Height:	3 ½", 8.9 cm
Colour:	Pooh: golden brown; brown and cream and red pots; green grass with multicoloured flowers
Issued:	June 2000 to the present

PRICING DATA	U.K. £	U.S. $	Can. $
Made Abroad	13.00	—	—

TABLEAUX

POOH™, PIGLET™ AND TIGGER™ TABLEAU

TECHNICAL DATA

Model No.:	A0410
Modeller:	Richard Wawrzesta
Height:	5 ½", 14.0 cm
Colour:	Pooh: golden brown; Piglet: pink with green clothing; Tigger: orange with black stripes; blue balloon; pink foxgloves; brown tree stump; green grass with multicoloured flowers; yellow butterfly
Issued:	June 2000 to the present

PRICING DATA	U.K. £	U.S. $	Can. $
Made Abroad	30.00	—	—

POOH'S™ WISHING WELL

TECHNICAL DATA

Model No.:	A0103
Modeller:	Richard Wawrzesta
Height:	7 ½", 19.1 cm
Colour:	Pooh: golden brown; Piglet: pink with green clothing; Tigger: orange with black stripes; Eeyore: grey and black; grey well with brown roof
Issued:	Jan. 2000 to the present

PRICING DATA	U.K. £	U.S. $	Can. $
Made Abroad	75.00	—	—

WALL PLAQUES

POOH™ PARTY

TECHNICAL DATA

Model No.:	A0422/A0423
Modeller:	Richard Wawrzesta
Height:	6 ¾", 17.2 cm
Colour:	1. Brown frame; multicoloured image
	2. Blue frame; multicoloured image
Issued:	June 2000 to the present

PRICING DATA	U.K. £	U.S. $	Can. $
Made Abroad	25.00	—	—

TIGGERS™ DON'T CLIMB TREES

TECHNICAL DATA

Model No.:	A0420/A0421
Modeller:	Richard Wawrzesta
Height:	7 ½", 19.1 cm
Colour:	1. Brown frame; multicoloured image
	2. Blue frame; multicoloured image
Issued:	June 2000 to the present

PRICING DATA	U.K. £	U.S. $	Can. $
Made Abroad	20.00	—	—

INDICES

ALPHABETICAL INDEX

MODEL NUMBER INDEX

BEATRIX POTTER

BRAMBLY HEDGE

FAIRIES

LEGEND OF KING ARTHUR

OLIVER OTTER AND FRIENDS

PETER PAN